BY STONY PATHS

❖❖❖❖❖❖❖❖❖❖❖❖❖❖❖❖❖❖❖❖❖❖❖❖❖❖❖❖❖❖

A version of Psalms 51–100

JIM COTTER

SHEFFIELD
CAIRNS PUBLICATIONS
1991

© Copyright by Jim Cotter 1991
ISBN 1 870652 11 8

First published 1991

Further copies of this book are obtainable from
Cairns Publications
47 Firth Park Avenue, Sheffield s5 6HF

The first volume in this series, *Through Desert Places,*
is also available

The third volume, *Towards the City,*
is in preparation

Printed by J. W. Northend Ltd
Clyde Road, Sheffield s8 0TZ

CONTENTS

iv   *Contents*

PREFACE

LIKE the first volume in this series, *Through Desert Places,* these fifty psalms are neither translation nor paraphrase of those numbered 51 to 100 in the Hebrew Psalter. Rather has the aim been to re-shape them so as to make them more directly prayable today. Weaving in and out of ancient themes and prayers are images and experiences derived from the New Testament and the twentieth century.

Along with each psalm there is a suggested refrain, which can be used as a group response at the end of each section. There is also a prayer reflecting the theme of the psalm: it could be used at the end, after, say, a period of silence.

A more extended introduction to the three volumes (the third, *Towards the City,* is planned for 1992 or 1993) is to be found at the beginning of the first book. The introduction to this volume explores one of the most difficult questions that any religious faith has to explore in every generation: How is it possible to reconcile a belief in a loving God with the excessive amount and degree of suffering in the world?

Dr Sheila Cassidy has had to face that question more acutely than most of those who will use this book. I am grateful to her for writing a more than generous Foreword...

I also want to acknowledge the inspiration of Daniel Berrigan in a book now out of print, *Uncommon Prayers,* in which he sought to bring the realities of life in mid-century America to bear upon the Psalms. I particularly have in mind the refrain to Psalm 53. My memory tells me that Psalm 73 owes a good deal to some reflections of Frank Lake, but I'm afraid I cannot trace the reference, and I apologize if copyright has been infringed.

JIM COTTER
Sheffield, January 1991

FOREWORD

I HAVE a theory that you can tell a lot about people by knowing which version of the Psalms they read. There are the King James people who love the ancient forms of the Authorized Version of the Bible with its Thees and Thous and the mystery of an archaic form and who writhe in pain at the very thought of the Good News Bible. Then there are the Roman Catholics of the sixties (and later) who have been raised on Gélineau and the scholars who mutter that the New Jerusalem Bible is nearer to the Hebrew. The Feminists have a non-sexist version in which the word God replaces every other synonym for the Deity except Yahweh, which everyone knows (or should know) should NEVER be voiced aloud! So where does this version fit in? What sort of people read Jim Cotter, and why?

The answer is, A lot of discerning people, including me! I first stumbled over Jim Cotter's writing in the bookshop at Exeter Cathedral when I picked up a little book called *Prayer at Night*. I was entranced. Here was Compline both familiar and different, in a language that made my heart sing.

> Broken are our bones, yet you can heal us,
> And we shall leap for joy and dance again.

I'd used *Prayer at Night* for several years before I discovered that Jim Cotter lived less than fifty miles away. I called on him and we became friends. Over the years I have grown to know and love his writing more and more.

By Stony Paths, Jim's version of Psalms 51–100, is a treasure trove indeed. Let me unpack it a little for you. But first I ask you to do one thing: put your own favourite version of the Psalms on one side and read these with an open heart. If you *don't* do that, you'll be distracted by trying to compare them and you'll miss the richness of this work. I say this because Jim's version is not so much a translation as a re-working, a re-fashioning. It is as if he has taken a collection of clothes, unpicked them, and then made a new garment out of each. Sometimes the result is only a mild variation, but others are radically cut, exciting, and very different. Take Psalm 53, for example:

> Acid in the rain shrivels the leaves,
> the wind rattles in the city's throat.
> Cancerous fish float down the rivers,
> even the innocent grass is corrupted.
>
> We have become as appetites in nightmares,
> as horses of apocalypse with thundering hooves,
> like monsters with ravening jaws,
> devouring what was given us to cherish.

Here I find Jim Cotter at his best: the poet with vivid images and words that sing, the prophet warning us that we are destroying the earth, and the priest reminding us of God in our midst. This powerful image of the rape of the earth and the pollution of the seas is a favourite of Jim's, born of his deep rootedness in the reality of our time and place. I love too his consciousness of the urban side of God: the God who has pitched his tent in the inner city:

> The streets of our cities are deserted,
> the rich and the strong have fled to the hills.
> The flowers of the park turn to weeds,
> the slides of the children rust.
>
> [Psalm 69]

> I search for you in unexpected places,
> at the edges of the known, in the language of dreams,
> in the wilderness of the city streets,
> in the grim towers where the desperate dwell...
>
> With food, shelter, and clothing we shall be content;
> with simple dignity we shall be rich in friends.
> The streets and squares of the city will be our meeting place,
> among the trees of the parks we shall breathe free and play.
>
> [Psalm 63]

In the first of these two stanzas from Psalm 63 we catch a glimpse of another side of Jim: the spiritual and psychological counsellor. Here we have a wisdom and understanding of the

human spirit not available to the earliest psalm writers: the
interface between the conscious and the unconscious mind and
the relationship between soul and psyche. In Psalm 77 he gives a
stunning vision of the soul's journey through the blackness of the
Dark Night of spiritual desolation to a knowledge of God that we
can neither name nor see.

> Drenched in sweat I lie on my bed,
> in the grip of delirium and fever.
> There is nothing to cool me and comfort,
> a terrible darkness descends.
>
> I stretch out my hands and my soul,
> yearning towards you from the depth of the night.
> I think on your name but see nothing:
> exhausted, my spirit faints.
>
> Disconsolate, I pluck at the strings,
> unable to hear the music we made,
> eye to eye loving each other,
> with melody in our hearts.

With the poet's skill he moves easily from image to image:

> Paralyzed in terror, my eyes stare wild;
> gripped by fear, I am weighted to the ground.
> Like a rabbit dazzled by headlamps
> I am dazed and cannot flee.

Then, as is the way of things, we move from desolation, despair
and terror through to that mysterious knowledge of the
unutterable holiness of God, the God who smashes our idols,
whose love demands all that we have.

> And yes, you are holy indeed,
> leading us beyond all that comforts us.
> Of course we must expect not to see you,
> when you leave no trace of your passing.
>
> Narrow is the path, no room for another,
> thin is the air, no breath to name you,
> thick is the cloud, there is nothing we can see,
> lonely is the way, no companions now.

Veiled in mystery, yet you are God.
Dark is the night, yet your glory transforms it.
Revealed in Jesus, yet a stranger so often.
The Unknown That Shalt Be, yet the hope of our future.
                                                [Psalm 77]

So there you have it: Cotter the poet, the prophet, the counsellor, the man of prayer. And, lest I forget, the writer of prayers. At the end of each psalm there is a short prayer, a drawing together of the themes of the psalm. In some ways, I think the prayers surpass the psalms, for they are pure Cotter, unbounded by preconceived ideas or forms:

> Harness the seething power of our anger, O God, the whirlpools of rage, the waves of indignation, and channel this awesome energy in the ways of your justice and love, in Jesus Christ our Doom and our Saviour.   [After Psalm 58]

And, lastly,

> O God, the same yesterday, today, and for ever, though we sense your absence in a bleak despairing time, focus our minds and hearts on memories of grace surprising us, that faith may be kept alive and hope re-kindled.   [After Psalm 77]

Amen to that.

                                        SHEILA CASSIDY
                                        Plymouth, November 1990

INTRODUCTION

LIKE the psalmists, we have experiences which shake faith's foundations, making it seem impossible to believe in God. The psalm itself is often a temporary resting place in a process of prayer in which, little by little, these lumps of experience are chewed and digested, and begin to be transformed into a living body of words, reaching to the depths of the imagination and of the flesh to renew and inspire. As we look at a psalm composed more than two thousand years ago, we may forget the cost of writing it. We may delight in the poem and call it well-wrought, forgetting that it was sweatingly and finely wrought, like intricate ironwork refined in the fire. And the author will undoubtedly feel wrung out. From time to time it will be worth the suffering. For through the refining and the transforming a psalm that begins with rage or anguish or complaint ends with praise.

The psalmists faced the disasters of defeat and exile which overtook their people. Has God broken those promises made in solemn covenant? In sorrow and exile, can the God of the homeland reach us? Will God come quickly and raise up the downtrodden? And, constant question, Why do the wicked prosper? Why this pain-wracked illness which obscures the face of God? Through all their questions they refuse to let go of God and refuse also to let go of a vision of a just order in community life. Theirs is a stubborn and argumentative praise.

In his poem, *Christmas 1921*, Rilke showed that he belonged to that same tradition:

> Say, Poet, what is your job? I praise.
> But those deadly, monstrous things,
> How do you endure them, grapple them? I praise.
> And then the Nameless, the Anonymous,
> How can you nevertheless invoke it? I praise.

So to the questions that arise in the midst of the faith-shattering realities of the twentieth century. Can we weave them in and out of those ancient cries and shouts, questionings and wonder? Can they find expression in a re-shaping of these poems? For there is much that will seem to stop us saying, even stubbornly, I praise.

When we are trying to come to terms with some particularly intractable bit of experience there will come a moment when words are no longer of use to us, when prayer seems empty and God absent and silent. At such times the words of psalms may point to that stage and enable us to endure it.

But the irony is that the psalms themselves are cast in the form of address to God, occasionally with God's reply. Now that works as long as the model of prayer as conversation is available to us. And most of the time this model is unavoidable. Indeed, if God is to be thought of as supra-personal and never less than personal, then it is almost inevitable that we shall carry within us the image of a supra-human being. After all, the personal is the highest category we know. So we may depict and address God as Father, Lord, Judge, Saviour. And in awareness of masculine bias we may extend the range of images and titles.

However, sooner or later we reach a point when one of two things happens. An image may become so powerful and dominant that we become addicted to it: it becomes an idol, dangerously obscuring the living God, indeed a substitute for the living God. We fear to smash the idol because we are reluctant to face the ensuing emptiness, the silence, the absence. The other possibility with the words and the image is that they become so well-worn as to be bland and no longer able to carry for us the meaning they once did. Again, the prospect is bleak.

We may then realize that we can never adequately *name* God. To do so would, in the old Hebrew understanding, to have gained control over God. And God would no longer be God. So there is no avoiding a silence at the centre of the words, however painful it may be. We have to become speechless and God silent. Yes, we may use more sophisticated phrases for God – Limitless Being, Limitless Love, Mystery of Being. We may simply breathe a whispered 'Thou'. But we have gone beyond the boundaries of language, beyond any easy consolations or sweetmeats of religion. And if Jesus himself lost the sense of intimate reverence in the presence of 'Abba', so we should not be too surprised to find ourselves in faithful and doubtful striving with a silent and absent God.

So the work done in this book on re-shaping the Psalms will have limited value, a fact which, I suppose, is both irritating and humbling to the writer. Yes, the language has been rendered more inclusive, both in terms of gender and in terms of a refusal finally to exclude enemies from one's own or God's presence. And yes, where the original has been written in the third person, descriptive of God acting, this has been changed into the language of address, 'You act', rather than 'He acts', thus making the prayer less distanced from us, more engaging.

But the irony remains that the very form itself is problematic in a time of awareness of God as Absent more than Present. Indeed, there are some who are convinced that there is no Reality beyond us who can ever be addressed as 'Thou', and that the spiritual task is to internalize the highest values of the Jewish-Christian tradition. Others have been so crushed by life that they can no longer make any sense of who or what God might be. R. S. Thomas's poem, *Christmas by the Sea,* in *The Echoes Return Slow* (Macmillan, 1988, p.84), imagines the Wise Men of Matthew 2 to be three waves of the sea who fall down and present their gifts "to what they don't understand".

Perhaps we have to hold in tension this sense of God as Absence, or a vast emptiness, a silent no-thing, and the increasing demand upon us that we no longer use God as a childish prop, but so grow into the 'god-liness' of the psalmists' prayer that we become in our own lives intimate co-creators with God, human faces of God in the world, actually moulding and making use of the pain and contradictions we experience. Such a task is awesome, especially when we reflect on the evils and pains of our time, and we may still find ourselves throwing our feelings of anger and injustice at an unheeding Deity. But this will be only the start of our spiritual journey.

Faith cannot by-pass the twentieth-century hells on earth, even if belief in hell as a place beneath the earth has declined. Just as God is no longer imaginable as simply 'over there', so hell is much nearer home. And there are few if any wildernesses left to which we can banish the 'fiendish' or 'demonic' as scapegoats for those realities that we lack the courage to face in our own back yard. If we can no longer do this personally, so too on a global scale, to aim to destroy an enemy utterly is to risk suicide and genocide. The lone gunman in the market town and the terrorist in a suburban den bring devastation home to each of us. Everything we pushed away is now, here, and among as well as within us.

Three people from our century can serve as illustrations of the scale of the spiritual task that human beings are now faced with: Primo Levi in relation to Auschwitz, Margaret Spufford in relation to genetic disease, and R.S. Thomas in relation to nuclear power.

Primo Levi, an Italian chemist, was imprisoned by the Nazis in Auschwitz. Under the pressure of that awful place he found his Jewish faith disintegrating. So it happened for Elie Wiesel: "Never shall I forget those flames which consumed my faith for ever."

Levi survived the camp because he had useful skills as a chemist. But he still had to endure the periodic assembly before a 'commission' which decided whether a person was still fit for work or should be assigned to the gas chamber. On one particular occasion he was in anguish and was tempted to cry out in prayer for help. But to do so would have been a kind of reverse blasphemy for an unbeliever. He rejected the temptation to call upon a supernatural being to intervene on his behalf. He comments that he would have felt ashamed.

Ironically, there is a misprint in Paul Bailey's Foreword to Levi's book, *The Damned and the Saved* (Michael Joseph, 1988, p.xviii). One sentence reads, "He kept faith with his faithfulness." An erratum slips corrects this to, "He kept faith with his faithlessness."

There is an austere integrity here, a truthfulness and clarity which enabled Levi to write of the Holocaust, not exactly with compassion and certainly not with forgiveness, but without hatred. He has refused to add to its pain. Such a refusal, held to for over forty years, might be seen as a kind of spiritual commitment. In an essay called *Against Pain* (in *Other People's*

Trades, Michael Joseph, 1989, p.184) he writes of the sheer quantity of pain which contaminates our lives and of the difficult task of each of us to diminish it as much as we can.

As a writer, he has done this by patiently, little by little, seeking to understand and communicate the details of everyday phenomena as well as the larger reality of the concentration camps. In writing about anything from chemical processes to chewing gum, his prose is cool and refreshing, luminous and firm.

Unlike Primo Levi, Margaret Spufford has held on to faith, but the process of coping with pain and the steady refusal to accept cheap consolation is remarkably similar to the attitude of the Italian. She has written of it in *Celebration* (Fount, 1989). She suffers from osteoporosis, a metabolic imbalance which causes the bones to fracture increasingly easily. She is an alive and alert woman in a slowly crumbling skeleton. Her daughter Bridget was born with a rare, genetically caused metabolic disease, cystinosis.

At one period she was surrounded by children on a ward in Great Ormond Street Hospital, all of whom were dying from diseases caused by genetic malfunction. She can call this none other than 'genetic evil', a malfunctioning from the moment of conception. She had to face the reality of small children who had been 'made wrong'. It was as if the hand of the Creator, visualized as a potter, had slipped.

Then there was the acute problem raised by the various treatments. Paediatricians had incidentally to hurt her daughter in order to get the diagnostic results both they and she wanted. At one time Bridget had to suffer six-hourly blood tests: she learned terror at the approach of a rattling trolley. What is the boundary of necessary pain? What is exquisitely refined torture? And what price God at the end of a therapeutic needle?

And through it all she lived with the roar of the waterfall of her own pain getting insistently louder.

Of all this 'tremendous bulk' (Primo Levi's phrase) of pain Margaret Spufford cannot even perceive how it could be transformed by love. It remains an intractable evil. She has found some help from the theologian W. H. Vanstone. For him the omnipotence of God is *not* total control, but a love that is able to bear whatever pain is heaped upon it and to redress what has grown amiss – even at the microscopic level of genetic failure. For Margaret Spufford to believe that is to have a faith finely wrought indeed, only just held on to and as fragile as her bones.

R. S. Thomas, priest and poet in Wales, has lived with a culture and language that has declined in the face of the English advance. He has lived among hill farmers scratching a raw living with whom he found it almost impossible to communicate in the language of faith. And he has watched nuclear power stations grow in beautiful places. He refers to himself as the composer of the first radioactive verses.

In one of his poems he writes of how we have opened a door of knowledge that we thought securely locked. On the other side of it we see a face wreaking vengeance, a kind of demonic wrath over against us that we cannot fathom, cannot turn to good, that may easily get out of hand, and that spreads an invisible poison. Only the most dedicated to science and prayer can draw near and not be harmed – and not pass on harm.

In trying to understand the detail of this new phenomenon in the human story, R. S. Thomas imagines that we are headlands that jut out into the sea, our fingers bleeding from searching blindly for what we fear we will find in the ocean depths.

To investigate or contemplate these things is to face horror. Such contemplation is not a contemplating of evil and then acting on it. It is a bearing within, a slow digesting, detail by detail. And we cannot yet call this Friday good.

So the Psalms present us with an ascetic work to be done. At times they may encourage us, but they do not flinch from awfulness and are not willing to let God get away with anything less than making all things come right. So we face the realities of genocidal murder, of genetic malfunctioning and its medical consequences, and of nuclear power, all new twists of pain in our century. We may occasionally glimpse fruits of understanding and compassion, but not always and never without cost.

It would be so easy to plunge with a dramatic leap of faith or
dive of despair. It is much harder to go step by step down the
rockface. In a poem called *Groping,* R. S. Thomas imagines a
dark cliff he is descending. He hears the voices of others
also climbing down. There are hands to take which help. Some
footholds and handholds have been used before. He thinks of
Wordsworth discovering poems that have been stranded on
ledges. And he discovers a faint light surrounding the bones of
those who have gone this way before, "pioneers who died
for truth."

There are then consolations, never as many as we cry out for,
but perhaps enough to strengthen us on the journey. There are
hands to stretch out and take, promises to make and keep.
Matthew Arnold on Dover Beach, as he watched the withdrawing sea of faith, exclaimed to his companion, "Ah love, let
us be true to one another." There are still the beauties of Nature,
even in cracks of concrete in the dereliction of abandoned sites of
industry. There are the artists who can still paint pictures for us
which seem like gifts that we never knew we were waiting for.
There are the symbols of sacrificial love, a crumb if not a loaf of
bread, a sip if not a draught of wine. Put together they do not
make it 'all right', but they are as real as the struggles of faith in
a dark time.

Step by step then. And who can say when faith might crack
and crumble for any one of us? There may come a moment when
we shall be able to do no other than plunge over the waterfall
whose roar Margaret Spufford hears and dreads. For reasons
unknown, Primo Levi plunged down the stairwell of his family
home in Turin and died one April day in 1987. It would be
improper to delve into the reasons why and too cheap to talk of
falling into the everlasting arms.

When we have done all we can, step by step down the cliff face,
we may be so exhausted that all we can do is to will a fall. Faith
may just give us the marginal hope that, in the last moment of a
total letting go, if the fall is into a bottomless pit, we may find
ourselves in a new world where gravity no longer exercises its
pull. We do know, from time to time, small moments of
transformation which we cannot compel yet we can in some way
work towards, moments which always surprise us because

they place some fear, some limitation, some problem into a wider context, a spacious room, an open landscape where there is room to breathe. Perhaps there lies ahead a totally unexpected transformation into a new dimension. The Spirit will no longer be imagined as Dove but as Eagle or Albatross, seizing us and teaching us how to fly.

But for the time being, the Psalms...

PSALMS 51–100

THE UTTER MERCY OF GOD

Refrain: Create in me a clean heart, O God,
and renew a right spirit within me.

Enfold me in your love, dear God,
yet pierce my heart with your mercy.
In the cascading of your compassion
scour away all that offends.
Wash me thoroughly from my wickedness,
and cleanse me from my sin.

My failures weigh heavy on my heart,
my sin confronts me at the turning of the road.
Against you alone have I sinned, my Beloved,
doing what is evil and causing more harm.
In the eyes of my victims your judgment is clear:
there is nothing I can claim in your presence.

I was formed in the midst of a world gone wrong,
from the moment of my conceiving I breathed my ancestors' sin.
The truths to which I am blind are hidden so deep, so secretly:
bring the light of your wisdom to the depths of my heart.

Bathe me in water that is fresh from the spring,
wash me and I shall be whiter than snow.
Make me hear of joy and gladness,
that the bones which you have broken may dance again.
Turn your face from my twists and deceits,
blot out all my misdeeds.

Cast me not away from your presence,
and take not your Holy Spirit from me.
Give me the comfort of your help again,
and strengthen me with your courage and hope.

Refrain: Create in me a clean heart, O God,
and renew a right spirit within me.

Then I shall teach your ways to those around me,
and others will be converted to your path.
Deliver us all from guilt of bloodshed, O God,
for you are the God of the world that is coming.
In health and truth we shall sing of your justice.
When you open my lips, O God,
my mouth shall sing of your praise.

For you desire no animal sacrifices,
no formal gifts out of mere duty.
You do not delight in burnt offerings,
nothing from our wealth can buy your favour.
The sacrifice you ask is a troubled spirit;
it is my pride that must yield.
My broken and contrite heart I bring,
so foolish, self-centred, and vain;
and yet it is all that I have.
Even this gift you will not despise,
for I hear again that you yearn for me,
with a love I can barely imagine.

So do I give you the whole of myself,
dependent as I am on the gift of your mercy.
So may my giving to others
be free of the motives of power,
gifts that overwhelm or appease.
May my heart be spontaneously giving,
spreading delight and mutual embrace.
Such is the way of the City of Peace,
whose walls you call us to build.

Take us to yourself, Compassionate God, we who hurt so much in the
depths of our being, caught up in the pain of life, and so often inflicting yet
more on to others; embrace us with the hands that show still the mark of
nails, your love swallowing up all our sin and pride. So we pray that broken
bones may joy, in the dance of Jesus our Redeemer.

THE LIE AND THE TRUTH

Refrain: Keep our eyes fixed on the truth,
the truth that will set us free.

So often the powerful ones of the world
seem to boast of their mischief and pride.
They trust in the abundance of wealth,
they take perverse delight in their greed.

They contrive destroying slanders:
their tongues cut sharp like a razor.
In love with evil they refuse the good:
telling lies, the truth is far from them.
They love words that harm and devour,
and every deceit of the tongue.

They step on one another as they climb to power,
they thrust the weak to the gutter;
seducing the gullible in the magic of words,
they trample the truth in pursuit of ambition.

O God, break them down utterly,
uproot them from the land of the living,
topple them from their Babel of lies,
throw them down to the dust.

Yet so often we are the powerful,
if only with family and friends.
We wound with whispers of gossip,
mockery and scorn in our hearts,
bitterness souring our lips.

Refrain: Keep our eyes fixed on the truth,
the truth that will set us free.

We have not trusted your goodness, O God,
our hearts have not been grateful.
We have not glorified your name,
neither by word nor by deed.

Too easy to call on God to destroy,
hard to be humbled by words that are true.
Even as we cry for the righting of wrongs,
for the destruction of those who harm others,
those who crush the weak and defenceless,
so do we know that revenge solves nothing,
annihilation reaping more violence still.

May your Spirit go deeper within us,
purging our hearts, burning the impure.
Hold at bay our murderous words.
May we strive with the angel of justice,
living the way of your truth and your Word,
our faces etched in the fierceness of Love.

Keep before us the vision of a life that is whole:
may we no longer grasp at material things.
Like a green tree may we spread out our branches,
to shield the passerby from the heat,
offering the traveller refreshment and rest,
in quietness and confidence living for others,
people of truth and compassion,
oases of God in the most barren of lands.

May our eyes turn to look again on you, O Christ. For you are the Way, the
Truth, and the Life. Give us courage always to be loyal to the Truth, to
follow wherever the Way may lead, costly though it be, trusting that the goal
is none other than Life in you.

FLESH OF OUR FLESH

God walks the earth,
a wandering Jew,
a holy fool,
in search of justice.

Acid in the rain shrivels the leaves,
the wind rattles in the city's throat,
Cancerous fish float down the rivers,
even the innocent grass is corrupted.

We have become as appetites in nightmares,
as horses of apocalypse with thundering hooves,
like monsters with ravening jaws,
devouring what was given us to cherish.

God walks the earth,
a poor man in rags,
peering into the darkness
for one face of trust.

We have raped the good earth and her peoples,
tearing them apart to satisfy greed.
We have relished the flesh of our neighbours,
like lions tearing their prey.

The powerful prepare a cannibal feast,
harsh eyes glint in the sharpening knives.
They have become as flesh-eating gods;
we, blind consumers, we follow them.

God walks towards us,
vulnerable as flesh,
a body broken,
blood shed.

Weighed down with bloodlust our footing slips,
we begin to drown in the floods of despair.
O God, grasp the hand stretched out in panic,
before we vanish for ever and are no more seen.

Forgetting the early days of our pain,
afraid of the intimacy we desperately crave,
we have speared the flesh of our neighbour,
refusing to draw near in healing embrace.

*Intimate God, Flesh of our flesh, Earth of our earth, reveal to us the anger
and malice, the greed and pride, that mask our pain; enable us to withdraw
the spear of our revenge from the flesh of others and from your flesh, O God.
Enclose our hurt in your side that we have wounded, and draw us closer to
one another in compassion and forgiveness, dependent utterly on your mercy
and acceptance.*

A CRY OF COMPLAINT

Refrain: O God, act soon.

Helpless, hemmed in, we are trapped by the powerful;
the insolent lash out with their tongue.
The ruthless sweep away what we thought were our homes,
the ignorant blame us because we are poor.

O God, are you not more powerful than they?
Why do you not speed them down to their doom?
Sweep them away who would treat us as worthless,
that we may feast our eyes on their fall.

What kind of God are you, my helper?
Why do you not show the strength of your arm?
You have promised to put an end to their power,
yet the promise remains unfulfilled.

Just once we have seen the world overturned,
your Chosen One vulnerable yet strong,
absorbing the evil thrown by the powerful,
triumphant through death in the ways of your love.

To keep trust with you taxes our faith,
to praise you in our days with hearts that are glad.
Why do you let the powerful still trample us down,
how can we believe when a child screams with pain?

Yet still we desire the face of your love,
to praise you in wonder for all that you do,
to know the scales fall from our eyes,
to dance the way of freedom hand in hand with the powerful.

*Spirit of the living God, deftly and quickly probe the diseased heart of our
world, and dissolve the evil encrusted there, that healed of our wounds and
rescued from our wrong, we may no longer oppress but set one another free,
in that same Spirit of Jesus Christ our Saviour.*

DAYS OF BETRAYAL IN THE CITY

Refrain: Renew the covenant of your love, O God:
          may we in truth be your friends.

In these our days of turmoil,
of restlessness and complaint,
we accuse and betray one another,
lashing out in the fury of pain.

We set on one another with greed,
we persecute with baying and clamour.
We see slaughter and our hearts writhe,
the horrors of dying overwhelm us.

Violence reigns in the streets of the city,
vicious dogs snarl at the stranger.
Fraud flits through the market place,
greed wins softly behind baize doors.

My eyes flash wild with horror,
my limbs quake and I cannot still them.
My heart grows cold through fear,
the ice of death grips me.

I said. O for the wings of a dove,
that I might fly away and be at rest.
I yearn to flee to the mountains,
to make my dwelling in the wilderness.

O for a refuge of peace,
out of the blast of slander,
far from the tempest of calumny,
from the harsh wind of the double-tongued.

For it was not an enemy who taunted me,
or I might have been able to bear it.
It was not a foe who was so insolent,
or I might have hidden myself away.

But it was you, my equal,
my companion, my familiar friend.
Ours was a pleasant harmony
as we walked side by side to the house of our God.

You have not kept your word,
you have no love of God in your heart,
and have broken the covenant you have sworn,
deserting those who were at peace with you.

Your mouth is smooth as butter,
yet war is in your heart.
Your words are softer than oil,
yet your sword flashes in the dark.

My heart cries out in anguish and grief,
Get out of my sight, you hypocrite!
Go down in terror to your grave, you betrayer,
for you have worked treachery among us.

Yet how I yearn for the healing of pain,
for a love grown cold to kindle again.
I pray to you, God, that we may be reconciled,
drawn again to the way of your justice.

Humble the pride in us all,
your love and your power consistent forever.
May we lift the weight of oppression,
may our enemies release the spring of their traps.

I cast my burden on you, O God,
and you will sustain and encourage me.
I will call from the midst of my groaning,
you will redeem me to healing and peace.

My heart has been so constricted,
my affections so easily hurt.
Yet your arms are wide and welcoming,
in your presence we are relaxed,
and feel most strangely at home.

O living God, whose love has been betrayed and denied over and over again, whose covenants have been torn apart, forgive our lack of trust and loyalty, and call us to yourself again, we who bear the marks of Judas and of Cain.

EMPTY AND AFRAID, YET TRUSTING

Refrain: I will put my trust in you, O God,
I will praise you for your Presence.
I will trust and not be afraid:
what can mortal flesh do to me?

The echo of the infant sounds,
the unwanted child cries for affection.
The giver of my life is my adversary,
persistently pressing upon me.
I feel nothing but hatred towards me,
I stand on no ground of my worth.
Are my tears counted in your flask,
are my hurts noted in your book?

I feel I am dying before I am born,
my feet slip from under me.
Empty and distressed, I am nothing,
yet I yearn for life to the full.

From the midst of my wasteland
of needs never met,
knowing my emptiness,
I wait to be filled.

Rain on the desert of my terror,
fill my empty soul to overflowing,
that I may joy in the life that you give,
a river that will flow to those who are parched.

As Mary opened her will, her heart, and her womb, giving her emptiness
to be filled with your living presence, so, Giver of life, encourage us to be
empty and open before you, that, being born in us, you may displace all our
fear and distress.

IDENTITY IN THE CITY

Refrain: Be exalted, O God, in your little ones,
let your glory shine in our streets.

The crowds on the pavements jostle me,
the drone of the traffic wearies me.
In the shadow of your wings I find refuge,
beneath your hovering presence I find peace.

The faces of strangers stare through me;
aimless I wander, there is nowhere I belong.
In the compassion of your face I find mercy,
in you and you alone do I know who I am.

I fear the hard glint in their eyes,
whose teeth snap from behind locked doors.
In the faithfulness of your promise I trust,
giving us freedom and wide open space.

Their faces look careworn and hollow,
grey like the evening and houses around.
Let melody break through the gloom,
the trumpet and flute to awaken the morning.

Compassion and care is locked in each one of us,
faithful and kind we all long to be.
Melt the fear in our hearts of the stranger we meet,
that we may open our arms in vulnerable embrace.

O God of freedom, unlock the hearts of your people who strive to be human
in the city, that your love may cast out fear, and that we may know again
that we belong to one another and to you.

WHAT KIND OF VENGEANCE?

Refrain: The faces of the downtrodden accuse us:
only the poor can redeem.

Do you decree what is just, O rulers of the nations?
With justice do you judge the peoples of the earth?
No, you work in the land with an evil heart,
you relish the violence you have wrought.
The wicked are estranged even from the womb,
they are liars that go astray from the day of their birth.

They are poisonous with the venom of serpents,
like the deaf asp that stops its ears,
that will not heed the voice of the charmers,
though the binder of spells be skilful.

Break their teeth, O God, in their mouths,
shatter the jaws of the young lions, O God.
Let them vanish like water that drains away,
let them be trodden down and wither like grass,
like a woman's miscarriage that passes away,
like an abortive birth that sees not the sun.

Let them be cut down like thorns before they know it,
like brambles swept angrily aside.
The just shall rejoice when they see your vengeance,
they will wash their feet in the blood of the wicked.
People will say, There is a reward for the virtuous,
for the wicked there comes the judgment of God...

Purge away from me, O God,
all malice and hatred, all bitterness of memory.
Stop my rejoicing at the pain of their doom,
even the worst of those who oppressed me.

Refrain: The faces of the downtrodden accuse us:
only the poor can redeem.

Only so can I hope to stand in your presence,
for you read all my ways and my heart,
all its murky unease and its fickleness.
We are all unjust, disordered, and lawless,
hardly sensing the lure of your love:
we can but know it as wrath.

Withhold your Light – it will blind us,
yet let us not perish in the dark and the cold.
Gradually warm the hearts that are frozen,
till the depths of the darkness dazzle.

Have mercy upon us, have mercy,
criminals and judges with the roughest of justice.
No plea can we enter before you.
It is the deprived and homeless, ragged and shivering,
who stand in the dock to accuse us.

Those on the edge, unkempt, unacceptable,
they are the ones who show us your face.
And, deep within, is a child who is shunned,
whom we treat as our enemy, battered and bruised.

O when will we learn to stretch out our arms,
to receive from the outcasts and scapegoats
the redeeming embrace and the melting of tears:
in them and them only is our last dying hope.

Harness the seething power of our anger, O God, the whirlpools of rage, the
waves of indignation, and channel this awesome energy in the ways of your
justice and love, in Jesus Christ our Doom and our Saviour.

FOR THE IMPRISONED AND TORTURED

Refrain: Judge and saviour of the world,
have mercy upon us, have mercy.

Cruel men roam the streets in the darkness,
howling like dogs, they prowl round the city,
They snarl and snap as they seize their prey,
they growl if their desire is frustrated.

I pray for the tortured and victims of malice,
for those imprisoned for no fault of their own.
My feelings run high – God forgive my excess –
why is your mercy and justice delayed?

Deliver the oppressed from the terrors of evil,
free them from those who relish their pain.
For the savage stir up violence against them,
waiting to knock at the door before dawn.

They keep the peacemakers distracted and tense,
breaking their spirit, mauling their flesh,
and all for no sin or transgression,
or any crime for which they are guilty.

The oppressed look to you, God their strength:
arise from your sleep and do not delay.
May your eyes flash with judgment and truth,
silencing the treacherous and false.

Show them the height of their pride,
reveal to them the lie they have lived.
Bind them so that their power is removed,
bring to their eyes the tears of repentance.

In your great love run to meet those who suffer,
show them the ruin of those who oppressed them.
Yet slay not the wicked, copying their ways,
but make them powerless to harm, and bring them to truth.

Refrain: Judge and Saviour of the world,
have mercy upon us, have mercy.

O God, from the depth of your love bearing pain,
break the cycle of our wraths and our sorrows.
For you are not a God who destroys,
you seek always to redeem and renew.

And so I will sing of your love and your power,
I will sing in the morning and tell of your goodness.
For you have been our strong tower,
a sure refuge in the day of distress.
I will sing your praise, O God my strength,
for you are my kraal for ever.

O God, seeking always to create at the heart of our evil and pain, sustaining
life in all your creatures and present with them in their distress, let us not
fall beyond your reach, and raise us by forgiveness and healing to a new love
for one another and for you.

THE WAR OF THE UNHOLY

Refrain: Turn us O God from our slaughter,
yet keep us striving for truth.

Echoes of warriors sound through the years,
we are zealous for God, holy our war.
We shout for you, our God, resplendent in armour,
your banner unfurled as we sweep into battle.

The fleet sails and our eyes shine;
our cause is just, our God is with us.
You are angry, O God, with our enemies –
we can slaughter them all, feeling no shame.

O God, do not be lukewarm and bland:
be provoked still by our enemies.
Do not storm out of sight through the dust,
leaving us to tremble in fear.

Yet you vanished from our sight: where were you?
You betrayed your promise to be with us.
Wounded and weary, we limp back defeated;
bewildered, we cling to your flag.

Are we far from the cry of the zealot,
from the mob who follow the drumbeat?
So easy to spit out the slogans of hate,
to become like those who oppose us.

So easy to swoop on the spoil,
to claim another parcel of land,
to grind the poor to submission,
to be drunk on the shedding of blood.

Refrain: Turn us O God from our slaughter,
yet keep us striving for truth.

Though we cling to belief in your blessing,
you are the God of island and continent,
and we but one race spread over the earth,
not one of us favoured above all the rest.

Our common greed and our fear of each other,
our desire for Mammon grown to excess,
our zeal for being right and others so wrong,
these are our enemies now.

In your name alone will we triumph,
content to be stewards of earth,
to live in justice with our neighbours,
the power of the fanatic taken away.

Forgive us, O God, for stubbornly continuing to picture you with iron fist, for claiming that you are always on our side. Renew the vision of you as wise and just guardian of the people, curbing the power of those who would harm, bearing in yourself what is yet unresolved. Keep us steady and true, that those we now perceive as our enemies may come to be our partners in the work of your creating.

HOPE IN GOD ALONE

Refrain: In our despair give us hope;
in our death give us life.

I stand on a rock at the edge of the sea,
the wind hurls the spray at my face.
The depths of the ocean swell heavy with menace,
tides of despair drown my heart in the deep.

I collapse by a rock in the wastes of the desert,
the noonday sun scorches my skin.
Waves of heat beat upon my weary heart,
my eyes stare at the dry bones around me.

The spirit has gone out of me,
my self-centred desires are as nothing.
I have come to the brink of inner death,
I descend to the depths of my doom.

Rescue me, O God, pity the pitiful,
lend me the strength of your tower of rock.
Succour me under your hovering wings,
welcome me into your hospitable home.

My vows lie broken, yet would I serve you,
my heart's desire is to love your name.
May the angels of mercy and truth stand by me,
the hand of deliverance heal me.

With a glimmer of hope I remember your love,
the love that finds me even as I search.
You have entered the void of my despair,
meeting me in the very place of your absence.

The music of praise sounds again in my heart,
the words of rejoicing take shape on my lips.
You renew my strength to fulfil what I promise,
the name that you give me endures through the years.

Implacable God, face us with the truth that we have no power of ourselves to help ourselves. Raise us from the depths of exhaustion and despair, and renew in us the spirit of life and hope, in Jesus Christ our Redeemer.

HOLDING STEADILY TO GOD

Refrain: Keep our eyes fixed on the goal,
Christ in us, the hope of our glory.

In the depths of my being I become quiet and still:
I wait for you, my God, source of my salvation.
You are a sure and steady rock, watching over me,
so that I shall not fall to my doom.

I am afraid of the powerful who overwhelm me,
cowards who encircle me, towering above me.
They are like a battering ram to a crumbling wall,
they exult in their lust for destruction.

Their delight is only in lies;
the truth is far from their hearts.
They utter words that are softer than butter;
inwardly they do but curse.

Nevertheless, I hold steadily to you:
you are my hope, my rock, my salvation.
In the stillness I wait for your presence:
you watch over me, I shall not fall to my doom.

In you, O God, is my health and glory,
the rock of my faith; in you is my trust.
I pour out my whole being in your presence:
in you I place all my hope.

In very truth we are but a breath of wind:
faithless and fearful, we have betrayed you.
Put us in the balance and we can only rise:
we are lighter than a feather in the wind.

Let us not trust in extortion and robbery,
let us not put on the masks of vanity.
When riches and possessions increase,
let us not set our heart upon them.

Refrain: Keep our eyes fixed on the goal,
            Christ in us, the hope of our glory.

For then we should become like the powerful,
betraying you again with our love of money,
trampling the face of the poor in the mire,
holding on to wealth by means of the lie.

Teach me again, O God, the truth of your name:
to you alone belongs power,
in you alone do we find mercy.
What reward could there be for our work?

*May the powerful of the land know their own failings and fears, and their
need for forgiveness, that they may empower the oppressed, temper the law
with mercy, and work for the common good, always holding before them the
vision of the Commonwealth of God.*

THE CITY-DWELLER'S DESERT

Refrain: Sustain me through the dry places,
        bring me to the beautiful country.

In the depths of my being you are my God,
at the rising of the sun I seek your face.
My heart thirsts for you, my flesh longs for you,
in a barren and dry land where no water is.

I search for you in unexpected places,
at the edges of the known, in the language of dreams,
in the wilderness of the city streets,
in the grim towers where the desperate dwell.

There may I look long and lovingly,
there may I listen for the word beyond words,
there may I wait for a glimpse of your glory,
there may I utter strange songs of your praise.

For your love endures to the end,
it is better even than life itself.
So shall my lips praise you,
and I shall lift up my hands in your name.

With food, shelter, and clothing we shall be content;
with simple dignity we shall be rich in friends.
The streets and squares of the city will be our meeting place,
among the trees of the parks we shall breathe free and play.

With manna in my exile do you feed me,
with water springing up from parched land.
I am deeply satisfied with a sumptuous feast,
my whole being resounds with murmurs of joy.

Refrain: Sustain me through the dry places,
bring me to the beautiful country.

Courage have I found to face the creatures of the night,
the terrible faces masking cries of abandonment,
swords that glint in the darkness protecting the weak,
jackals that swoop on those who dare near.

I am bewildered by mirrors distorting the truth,
lost before hallucinations spun in the heat.
Yet will I trust you through the blindness of light,
through the delusions that threaten to destroy me.

I hear your voice, Do not be afraid.
You sustain me in the watches of the night,
your hovering wings give me shade on my journey.
I stumble, yet I trust you not to let go.

The faces of terror will prove my friends yet,
guarding as they do my fragile soul-self,
waiting the calm word of the approach of true love,
waiting to be named as faithful and true.

So shall I emerge to the place of rejoicing,
the child and the adult linked arm in arm.
We shall see your face in all your creatures,
we shall know the truth in our hearts.

Pioneer of the living way, give us courage to traverse the waste and barren
places, trusting that we shall come at the last to our true home and to the city
of our God.

BEWILDERED BY CRUELTY

Refrain: I reel from blows of the enemy:
where can my heart find ease?

Hear me, O God, from the depths of my being,
fearful as I am of being destroyed.
Who are these enemies that swirl around me,
who conspire against me in a hostile world?

How have I released this torrent of abuse?
Whence come these arrows of bitter words?
Those whom I thought were my friends
pile all my faults on my tired spirit.

No innocence, O God, would I pretend,
my failure and guilt are too real.
But it feels they were planning in secret,
ready to pounce from a place unseen.

Through the years they smiled and spoke tenderly:
now the lash of their tongues is unleashed.
They have laid their mines with such skill –
they have even forgotten they did so –
and they blame me for stepping upon them.

Perhaps they did not even know what they did,
so dark and deep is the human heart.
They dare not face the truth of their pain:
they seek revenge for hurts unremembered.

Deliver me, O God, from the paralysis of fear,
from the confusions of my mind and the turmoil of my heart.
I am consumed with anxiety and dread,
the hovering unknown fills me with terror.

Refrain: I reel from the blows of the enemy:
where can my heart find ease?.

The sky seems full of probing eyes,
an unseen lens orbits the earth.
Ears hide in dim corners of the room,
the wavelengths carry our secret thoughts.

Reveal them to themselves, O God,
bring them down for the evil they have spoken,
those who say they hate only my sin,
but who slay me in the name of your justice.

Let the devices of our hearts be made known,
your arrows of truth piercing our confusions.
Reveal us in scorching light to one another,
that we may lay down our weapons and forgive.

Even now we rejoice and give thanks to your name,
the distortions of our being are eased gently through judgment,
the fierceness of your love is holding us upright,
the light of your eye shines with compassion and justice.

Dear God, we bring to you everything of which we are unaware, the
unknown murky devices of our fearful hearts, the untapped sources of
generosity and laughter, the forgotten confusions and hurts from which come
our excessive anger, the unrealised capacity for truth and forbearance.
Reveal us to ourselves and reassure us in the true humanity of Jesus Christ.

IN PRAISE OF GOD, ABUNDANT AND GENEROUS

Refrain: Let the people praise you, O God:
let all creation praise you.

We praise you God in your holy city,
we renew our vows in the holy places.
For you meet us in the depth of our being,
when we come to confess all that is true of us.
When our misdeeds haunt us with their power,
your generous love sweeps them aside.

Blessed are those whom you choose as your friends,
who lodge with you in your house.
You empower them with talents and gifts,
you crown them with an abundance of blessings.

In dread deeds you will deliver us,
O God of our salvation,
for you are the hope of the ends of the earth,
and of the distant seas.

By your strength you make the mountains rise,
by your power you gouge the valleys deep.
You still the raging of the seas,
the roaring of the waves,
and the tumult of the peoples.

Those who dwell at the ends of the earth
are held in awe at your wonders:
the dawn and the evening sing your praise.

You tend the earth and you water it,
you make it rich and fertile.
Your clouds are full of water,
they provide rain for the swelling grain.

Refrain: Let the people praise you, O God,
let all creation praise you.

You drench the furrows,
you level the ridges between,
you soften the soil with showers
and bless its early growth.
You refresh hearts withered AND dry,
you bring to life the land parched with drought.

You crown our years with good gifts,
the fruit trees drip with abundance.
The alpine pastures shimmer with green,
the hills are wreathed with dancing clouds.
The meadows are clothed with sheep,
and the valleys mantled with corn.

Loving God, ceaselessly redeeming and creating, astonish us with your
abundant generosity, and still our hearts in awe and wonder.

SYMPHONY OF PRAISE

*Refrain: Let the whole earth shout with joy to our God:
let all the people sing your praise.*

Let the earth give praise to you, our Creator,
let all the peoples of the world give you praise.
Let psalms ring out to your glory,
for awesome indeed are your works.
Those who would defy you are brought low,
and the peoples fall silent in your presence.

Let the people you have redeemed give you praise:
marvellous are the deeds you have wrought for us.
You turned the waters into dry land,
and we passed through the sea on foot.
So we rejoiced in your strength:
your redeeming power has no end.
Even though the rebellious rise,
your quiet strength quells them.

Let the people you have rescued give you praise,
let the sound of singing voices carry far.
You established us where we now dwell,
you keep us from all lasting harm.
Yet you test us as silver is tried,
you catch us in the nets of our weaving,
you let others ride over us roughshod,
you lay sharp torment on our loins.
No easy wealth or worldly applause
as we go through fire and water!
But you have borne our pain with us,
bringing us into a place broad and free.

Refrain: Let the whole earth shout with joy to our God:
let all the people sing your praise.

I too will add my morsel of praise
as I thank you for all you have done.
I have kept my vows in the teeth of distress,
tempted to hold back my offering.
But I bring my best gifts to your presence,
my possessions and talents, all that is yours.
When I cherished evil you brought me low,
and turned my twisted heart to face you again.
You heard the deepest voice of my being,
fain as it was, unknown to my clamour,
and you responded with grace unpredictable,
you never ceased in your love and your care.

Let the wordless cries of creation, and the shaped voices of the people, let the
deep sighs of each heart and the testimony of faithful lips, let all be joined
in a harmony of exultant praise to you, Beloved God, our Creator and
Redeemer.

GOD'S ABUNDANT BLESSINGS

Refrain: Let the people praise you, O God,
let all the people praise you.

God be gracious to us and bless us,
and show us the light of your countenance
and be merciful to us,
that your way may be known on earth,
your saving health among all nations.

Let the nations rejoice and be glad,
for you judge the people with wisdom,
and you guide the nations upon earth.

Then shall the earth bring forth the harvest,
and God, even our own God, shall give us great blessing.
Dear God, you will bless us indeed,
and all the ends of the earth shall praise your holy name.

O God of wise judgment, accepting us as we are and guiding us in your
ways, enable us so to appreciate your gifts of the harvest that we may know
them as a pledge of abundant life and thank you as the source and goal of all
that is good.

WHAT KIND OF POWER?

Refrain: We praise you, O God, for your power,
the power of the Way of Christ.

O God, humble and truthful,
scatter falsehood and bloated pride.
By the fierce light of your eyes
shrivel the power of the powers.
As smoke vanishes in the wind,
so shall they be dispersed.
As wax sizzles in the flame,
so shall evil squirm in your presence.
But justice and truth will be glad,
they will exult and rejoice.

We sing to you, O God,
we sing praise to your name.
We give you the glory
in the midst of our desert.
You come with living water
to dry and thirsty ground.
You are the father of the fatherless,
you are the mother of orphans,
you uphold the cause of the widow,
you give voice to the cries of the poor.
You give the desolate a home to dwell in,
you bring prisoners out of the dungeon.
Only those who complain and rebel,
who resent second place to the outcast,
know the storms of the desert within them,
feel the sun scorching their pride.

Like your people of old we delight in you,
glad of the home and the land which you give us,
which you put in our hands to care for.
Marching out as you do in the wilderness,
still leading us on by the pillar of fire,
you go on always before us,
preparing a place for your dwelling.
We bless you and give you thanks,
for you bear us as your burden.
You are to us a God who saves,
by your power we escape the pangs of death.

Even the snow-capped mountains shrink in your presence,
all the wealth of the nations is as nothing before you.
The power of the haughty is a broken reed,
our silver and gold worthless on your scales.
You quieten our shouts of triumph and victory,
as we see your rain refreshing our enemies.

Sing to God, O realms of earth,
sing praises to the God of the heavens,
who rides on the stormy wind,
whose voice thunders through the skies.
O God, you are awesome and terrible,
your light blinds even through clouds.
You give strength and power to your people,
to resist and scatter the relishers of war.

Refrain: We praise you, O God, for your power,
        the power of the Way of Christ.

Exuberant is our victory song,
yet we are no better
than those who oppose us.
We too are greedy for spoil,
self-righteous in slaughter.
Let us see you again
as you came to us,
contracted to the span of a child,
helpless in the arms of his mother,
compassionate in bearing
while pinned to a cross,
taking the trampling of blood
deep in the heart of your being,
breaking the barrier of death
to new and glorious life.

We fall silent before the mystery of love,
this renouncing of power familiar so long,
this reversal of power that none can defeat,
this wonder we can scarcely believe.

*Dear God, as we struggle to understand and use the power aright that you
entrust to us, set before us again the way of Jesus, and work through us in
your Spirit, that we may steward our power in ways that do not bind others
but free them to take their share in the inheritance of life. May we grow not
tall but humble.*

ANY HOPE FOR THE EARTH?

Refrain: The earth and the people decay:
        we breathe but a whisper of prayer.

Save us, O God: we are perishing!
The seas are swelling and flooding the land.
The rivers sweep away the soil laid bare,
the algae thickens off the summer coasts.

What is this weariness that grips us,
this cry of alarm that sticks in our throat,
the eye of conscience that no longer sees you,
the snap of hatred in those we thought wise?

We shame and disgrace our ancestors,
we betray those who come after us,
we rape the earth who mothered us,
we mock the few who stand for truth,
we have become as strangers to our children,
we are like aliens from a planet far away.

No longer is our word our bond;
we destroy trust by rumours and lies;
we find fault wherever we go,
we pillory those who are different.

We throw all the blame on to foreigners,
on to those in positions of power.
In truth there are few who are innocent,
the humble, the needy, the oppressed.
and vengeance is a luxury now.
The bombs and the guns of our fear
now destroy the earth and our neighbour.

In despair we are trapped and brought low,
unaware and unable to change.
We have even forgotten there may be a God,
a power beyond our own to whom we could cry.

Refrain: The earth and the people decay:
we breathe but a whisper of prayer.

In this our critical time,
is there a God who is good?
What price deliverance now,
as the very earth and the seas turn upon us?

Pride, greed, and malice all mock at us:
inordinate selfishness cries out in triumph.
With insults we break others' hearts,
we trample the weak to the ground.

We poison the food of our children,
the wine on our tables turns into vinegar.
We toss aside those we pretend we have loved,
our loins shake with disease.

The streets of our cities are deserted,
the rich and strong have flown to the hills.
The flowers of the parks turn to weeds,
the slides of the children rust.

We croak from the mire of the pit:
Let the echo of the walls be our prayer.
Let the menace of the waves turn to laughter.
Let the currents of the rivers dance.

From deep underground let the waters rise,
let them float us out of the caverns of darkness.
Let seeds of the trees be planted again,
let the clouds rain with pure water.

High on a cross a man hangs parched,
forsaken by friends and by God,
taking to himself their suffering and pain.
He dies with a cry – a whisper or howl? –
yet trusting the one who is absent.

Open our eyes again that we may see,
unfold our hearts to be open to your love.
May we greet our neighbours in trust,
and rebuild the walls of the city.

Be for us, O God, a deliverer still,
a God of compassion and joy.
Then will our mouths discover praise:
we will glorify you with thankful hearts.

As the sun returns to us in the depths of winter, come, O strange and terrible God, so often silent and hidden, rescue us from the brink of our doom, and renew the scarred face of the earth.

FAITH STRIPPED BARE

Refrain: Hold to the God who is absent,
trust in the God who withdraws.

The ruthless seek to destroy,
they hurt beyond repair.
Gaunt and hollow-eyed,
their victims limp to the grave.

Refused even their dignity,
they have no voice of their own.
Their faces press to the window,
they slink starving away.

The cruel are oblivious:
surely they would be appalled
by a conscience revived,
by eyes that were opened.

The cries of the needy are drowned
by their baying taunts of mockery.
Blind to the needs of the weak,
they dismiss them as merely a number.

The needy cry to the heavens,
to the Eagle with piercing eye.
But the skies are empty and cold,
no deliverer descends in our day.

Is there a God of compassion?
Is there a God of justice?
Is there One yearning in love?
Is there a God who can save?

Why do you delay your appearing?
Why do you keep us nailed to our pain?
Why do you harden the hearts of the cruel?
Why is our sense of you slipping away?

God, hard to believe in, bring us through dark nights of doubt to the joy in
which our ancestors danced your praise.

A PRAYER OF OLD AGE

Refrain: As the winds of winter gather,
do not forsake me, O God.

You have been the source of my strength, O God,
from before the day I was born.
You brought me forth from the womb,
you sustained me before ever I knew of you.
You were the confidence of my heedless youth,
you gave me my hope and my courage.

When I strove with the evil in my heart,
when I fought the enemies of your truth,
you refreshed me in the heat of the battle,
you were the rock in whose shade I recovered.
You were my stronghold on the mountain crag,
you were my refuge in the homes of my friends.

I have seen the eyes of the pitiless and cruel,
I have been wounded by words and by deeds.
I have been ignored and neglected by the powerful:
they pass over my name for promotion.
They have gossiped with glee at my failings,
they delight in rumour and lies.

My fate has filled many with awe:
I have become as a warning and portent.
And now I contend with old age,
withdrawing my eyes and my ears.
Few and grey are the hairs of my head –
no problem in numbering them now!

In this new testing of faith,
still would I praise you, my God.
I long for you still with hope,
and I will praise you more and more.
My mouth shall tell of your ways
to the generations taking my place.

Refrain: As the winds of winter gather,
do not forsake me, O God.

Yes, you have brought me through deep waters,
through trials bitter and troublesome.
You have burdened me yet given me strength,
you have raised me up from the depths.
Bless me now in the days of my fading,
turn to me again and give me your comfort.

Your just ways, O God, spread through the world –
great is the tale of your wonders.
I will make music in praise of your faithfulness,
through the days of my life and beyond.
I will sing of the mystery of Love,
my being soul-deep will rejoice in your name.

Even through the waters of death will you bring me,
keeping at bay my terror of drowning.
My lungs will fill with the breath of new life,
and I will praise you in the garden of delight.
We will dance as the poor enriched,
we will sing as the oppressed redeemed.

Those who knew not what they did,
and those who relished their malice,
even our enemies, through their shame and disgrace,
will be lured by the beauty of Love,
will weep at the music they spurned,
will at last speak the truth from their hearts.

As trust and doubt, distress and delight, success and failure, wax and wane
through the years, keep our eyes fixed on you, dear God, and give us courage
to face the trials and temptations that have yet to come our way.

A PRAYER FOR JUST AND WISE RULERS

Refrain: Give wisdom to those who govern,
who bear burdens on the people's behalf.

O God, give wisdom to those who govern us,
a sense of justice to those who wield power,
that they may frame laws that are life-giving,
that the poor and the weak may breathe freely.
May they defend the cause of the needy,
save the abandoned and orphans,
disarm the rebellious and violent.

May such wisdom endure like the sun and moon,
giving light from one age to the next.
May justice rain down like showers
that water the new-sown fields.
In our days may justice flourish,
and abundance of peace till the moon be no more.

May wisdom reign from sea to sea,
following the great rivers to the end of the earth.
May folly bow down to truth,
the enemies of justice lick the dust.
May all the rulers of the peoples seek wisdom,
the nations serve the ways of justice and truth.

Those who are wise deliver the needy when they call,
the weak and those who have no one to speak for them.
They will rescue them from oppression and violence,
and their lives are precious in their sight.

So may there be abundance of grain in the land,
to the tops of the hills may it wave.
Let the mountains be laden with peace,
with the prosperity that follows from justice.
May the corn swell with the gentle rains,
the sheaves thicken like the grass of the meadows.

Refrain: Give wisdom to those who govern,
             who bear burdens on the people's behalf.

May prayer be made for those in high office,
that they may bear their burdens with wisdom.
May blessings be invoked on them day by day,
may they be heartened by the prayers of the people.

Blessed be the God of all the earth,
who alone is all wisdom and justice,
who alone does great wonders.
Blessed be the glorious name of God:
may the universe be filled with God's glory.
Let the Amen echo with praise.

O God, the cry of our prayer and the reality of our politics are far apart.
Renew in all of us a thirst for justice, a cherishing of the earth and the
oceans, the wisdom of restraint, and a deep desire for the common good.

PERPLEXITY UNRESOLVED BUT TRANSFORMED

Refrain: Let us delve the deepest questions,
living their mystery.

To the loyal and loving and faithful,
God indeed is pure goodness.
And yet I was losing my foothold,
slipping and slithering from faith.
For I was envious of the boast of sinners:
without God they were entirely content.

They suffer no pains that I can see:
they look ever so healthy and sleek.
They never seem plunged into grief,
never harassed or thrown off course.
Pride is the signet ring on their finger,
craving for power fits them like a glove.

Their eyes gleam through folds of fat,
mirror of their empty minds.
Their faces ooze malice and greed,
their hearts brim over with the basest of thoughts,
with mocking laughter and cynical scorn,
overwhelming with menace and threats.
Their slanders are raised against heaven,
their tongue plies to and fro on the earth.

Of course they carry the mob with them,
lapping up their words like cheap wine –
What has God to do with us?
Are you still there?
Do you take any notice?
They go their godless way with a will,
untroubled they grow ever more wealthy.

Why did I ever keep faith with you,
why did I keep my conscience alert?
Every day is a punishment to me,
every morning I wake feeling beaten.

*Refrain: Let us delve the deepest questions,
living their mystery.*

I have often thought, Do like those others.
But then I would have betrayed the Body of Christ,
I would have denied the faith of my ancestors.
So I was tossed backwards and forwards,
perplexed, desperate, baffled by it all.

Then I turned to worship you, O God,
and I pierced the heart of the mystery.
I began to see you with a sword in your side,
I began to see life in the light of your future.

The life of the unheeding totters on quicksand,
keeling over and falling to ruin.
They are in one fell moment destroyed.
They are living in the shadow of nightmares,
evil dreams that haunt in the morning,
dreams that are suddenly ended,
as they fall to their doom, unmourned and forgotten.

Yes, the struggle for faith has cost me dear:
like Jacob I limp in the sunrise.
With the heart's blood alone is victory wrought,
the price of the whole of my being.
You have embraced me in the ocean wastes,
a bird whose wings are trapped in black oil.
You weave all my doubts and distress
to a pattern of dancing joy.

It was a bitter heart that made me rebellious,
I was hurt in the depth of my being.
Distraught, I hammered away at you:
deranged, I vented my fury.
Nevertheless you absorbed my rage,
you embraced me and held me,
drawing the poision out of my heart,
giving me rest and deep peace.

I do not see you, yet do I trust in you.
No wisdom or strength dare I claim as my own.
Yet still you uphold me, and receive me in glory.

Though my flesh is falling apart,
though my heart is strained to breaking,
though my bones ache in the winter,
though my blood runs thin in my veins,
nevertheless still you are God,
you are the future that waits for me,
How this can be is hidden from me,
you are the mystery giving no answers.
Yet I look to no one else in the universe,
with you I am well content.

Those who abandon you are doomed.
To break faith with you is to be lost.
True joy lies in drawing closer to God,
to the suffering, the mystery, the terrible love.
In you I believe that all shall be well.
So I will speak of your name and your ways,
not with a shouting that covers my doubts,
but a whisper sounding the depths of enduring.

*And yes, the questions trouble us still, perplexing God, and will do so to the
end of our days. Is there no way the pride of the powerful can be punctured?
Can we not learn to share the good things of the earth? Do we not collude
with those who are unjust? Do we not compensate too glibly with the
promise of good things after death? Nevertheless, nevertheless . . . So in the
midst of our questions, deepen our trust; in the midst of our trust, keep our
questions alive. Cleanse the eye of our perception and purify our hearts that
we may will one thing, that your way indeed be followed through and beyond
the perplexities we cannot escape. Glorify your name, O God, and justify
your ways!*

THE SEA OF FAITH?

Refrain: The tide of faith still ebbs:
Dare we work and wait for its turning?

The more we are aware, O God,
the harder does faith become.
The more we contemplate the desolation,
the further you seem to withdraw.

Millions die in the labour camps,
a child's scream pierces the night.
The chainsaws screech through the forests,
an elm withers in the meadow.

The desert sands creep onward,
acid rain crumbles the statues,
chemicals choke the rivers and lakes,
nuclear waste stores wrath in the earth.

Beautiful buildings decay into ruin,
exquisite carvings crumble to dust.
The places of prayer are too heavy for faith,
their very doors oppressive with weight.

You have deserted the altars, O God,
the faithful few ignore their decadence,
maintaining at extraordinary expense
that from which the meaning has departed.

Faith retreats into privacies,
or clashes with violent fervour.
The sensitive shudder and whisper,
the bullies shout and trample.

The grass of the arenas is scarred,
games turn to battles, the injured hobble.
New domes rise up from industrial waste,
temples for consumers at worship.

The voice of the prophet is thrown to the wind,
the springs of sacrifice run dry.
Service of others is measured by money,
those who would guide lack all sense of direction.

The tales of our faith falter,
the memory of God grows dim.
Did you really swoop down to rescue,
do you truly care for Jerusalem?

Did your hand strike the rocks of the desert,
and make the water flow?
Do you care for the sparrows' brood?
Do you give us manna in our wilderness?

Look on this earth of your creating,
see the billowing clouds of corruption,
listen to the trudge of the weary,
open your ears to the taunts of the mindless.

Dare we praise you, O God, do you hear our cry,
meeting it in the depths of your being,
giving yourself for us and all people,
the Lamb slain across aeons of time?

To the mystery of the Cross we hurl our questions,
and doggedly worry away at our doubts.
Yes, you absorb the wastes of our wraths and sorrows,
turning pain to glory in the vortex of Love.

O God, fading from our sight as our own sight grows dim, work still in us and through your world, till our eyes open to a strange and shocking light, a scarcely believable new dawn.

SURE JUDGMENT

Refrain: Come with the judgment that chastens,
come with the wounds that heal.

Love flashes like lightning,
cuts through the heart of evil,
shows up pride in its ghastly light,
surprises our hidden boasting.

Love thunders in judgment,
sounding from horizon to horizon,
searching the depths of our being,
proclaiming the truth from the rooftops.

In awe and wonder we look to you,
O God, creating anew through your judgment,
sovereign and free in discernment,
at last making things right.

You hold a strange cup in your hands,
foaming with wine, astringent with spices.
You give it to us to drink,
to test the extent of our wickedness.
We drain it down to the dregs,
and see ourselves as we are.

The wine like liquid flame
burns through the layers of evil.
Like a hammer to the skull,
it breaks the crusts of habit.

Drained of our evil we tremble,
empty and naked before you.
We would be glad of the rags of the starving,
so defenceless do we feel.

The oppressed and the dying look into our eyes,
stretch out their hands in their weakness,
not to receive – we have nothing –
but to lift us out of fear and despair.

In them do we see you, O Christ,
eyes so clear and compassionate,
forgiving our wrong at the cost of your life,
with wounded palms embracing us.

We praise you, dear God,
we give you the glory.
We will tell of your wonders,
of your judgment and mercy.

*Living Flame, refine us in the truth, burn out all that is impure with the fiery
eye of clarity, and warm into life the frozen battered child that longs to live
again.*

THE LION'S WRATH

Refrain: With dread deeds save us,
with wrath embrace us.

Heraldic you stand on the battlements,
radiant in the dawn of the day –
Lion of Judah, powerful and just,
more majestic than snow-capped mountains.

Jerusalem you claim as your own,
scattering the haughty and proud,
at a stroke snapping their arrows,
silencing their rebellion with a roar.

The men of war tremble,
there is no strength in their arms;
they stand aghast, helpless;
dumbfounded, they cannot speak.

You beat our swords into ploughshares,
you defeat all the wiles of our warring,
you terrify those who use terror,
the powerless and oppressed have nothing to fear.

Our human wraths hurt and destroy:
your wrath is clear in its justice,
a terrible love that drums in our ears,
insistent, compelling, triumphant.

Awesome is your promise to love us,
terrifying is the response you seek from us.
Our weapons of war lie broken before you:
your vow is fulfilled in our sight.

Lion of Wrath, we would cower from the prowling of your love, we would
slink into the prison we have made for ourselves. Give us your courage to face
our fear, break down our iron bars, in one bound rescue us despite ourselves.

PAST MERCIES, PRESENT DESPAIR, FUTURE HOPE

Refrain: Keep the memory of your goodness alive,
fan into flame the embers of hope.

In anxiety I murmur towards you,
in distress I cry out from my heart.
I call but hear only my echo:
Is God wrapped in silence for ever?
My eyes stream tears of sorrow,
groaning wells up from within.
Despair grips my heart like ice,
there is no breath in my lungs.

Drenched in sweat I lie on my bed,
in the grip of delirium and fever.
There is nothing to cool me and comfort,
a terrible darkness descends.
I stretch out my hands and my soul,
yearning towards you from the depth of the night.
I think on your name but see nothing:
exhausted, my spirit faints.

Disconsolate, I pluck at the strings,
unable to hear the music we made,
eye to eye loving each other,
with melody in our hearts.
Paralyzed in terror, my eyes stare wild:
gripped by fear, I am weighted to the ground.
Like a rabbit dazzled by headlamps
I am dazed and cannot flee.

Will you cast me away for ever?
Will you no longer surprise me with joy?
Is your mercy vanished for ever?
Have your promises come to end?

Refrain: Keep the memory of your goodness alive,
fan into flame the embers of hope.

Have you forgotten to be gracious?
Have you closed your heart to pity?
Have you broken that strong right arm?
Has your love no power to endure?

I suffer a sickness of soul:
I demand you live up to my image.
You are no idol to serve my desires:
Thou art Thou, living, mysterious, and free.
With numbed fingers I hold on to you yet,
like a climber on the face of a mountain.
Though the waves of the sea crash over me,
like a limpet I cling to the rock.

Dogged and grim, yet I remember the past,
the wonders of rescue, the God who acts.
I will think on the deeds you have done,
I will meditate on the God who acts.
You made known your power among the peoples,
by great deeds you redeemed your own.
You brought the children of Jacob and Joseph
from bondage to the promise of freedom.

The waters of the sea cowered back before you,
the voice of your thunder was heard in the whirlwind,
your lightning lit up the horizon,
the clouds poured down rain at your bidding.
Your path was through the Sea of Reeds,
and on through the trackless wastes.
The earth shuddered at your passing,
though your footsteps were not seen.

By the hand of Moses and Aaron,
you led your people out of slavery.
By the wounds of your Beloved on the Cross,
you led them through the pangs of death.

In times of exhaustion you lifted us up,
through closed doors you surprised us with joy.
Through the words of friends you have encouraged us,
through intimate touch you come close again.
And yes, you are holy indeed,
leading us beyond all that comforts us.
Of course we must expect not to see you
when you leave no trace of your passing.

Narrow is the path, no room for another,
thin is the air, no breath to name you,
thick is the cloud, there is nothing we can see,
lonely is the way, no companions now.
Veiled in mystery, yet you are God.
Dark is the night, yet your glory transforms it.
Revealed in Jesus, yet a stranger so often.
The Unknown That Shalt Be, yet the hope of our future.

O God, the same yesterday, today, and for ever, though we sense your
absence in a bleak despairing time, focus our minds and hearts on memories
of grace surprising us, that faith may be kept alive and hope re-kindled.

RIDDLES OF HISTORY

Refrain: Deluded, rebellious, estranged,
we know neither ourselves nor our God,
the God whose ways are mysterious,
an enigma, a question, a riddle.

Listen to my teaching, O my people:
incline your ears to the words of my mouth.
For I will open my lips in a parable,
and expound the mysteries of former times.
What we have heard and known,
all that our ancestors told us,
we will not hide from our children,
but declare to a generation to come:
the praiseworthy acts of God,
God's mighty and wonderful works.
O God, you established a law for your people,
you witnessed to your ways in Israel,
which you commanded our ancestors
to teach to their children,
that future generations might know you,
and children yet to be born,
that they in their turn might teach it
that their daughters and sons might trust you,
that they might keep your commandments
and not forget your works –
as did their ancestors,
a rebellious and stubborn generation,
a generation whose heart was warped,
whose spirit was not faithful to God.   *Refrain*

The children of Ephraim armed with the bow
turned back in the day of their battle.
They did not keep your covenant, O God,
they refused to walk in your law:
they forgot what you had done,
and the wonders you had shown them.
You worked marvels in the sight of their forebears,
in the land of Egypt, in the country of Zoan.
You divided the sea and let them pass,
you made the waters pile up in a heap.
In the daytime you led them with a cloud,
and all night long with the pillar of fire.
You cleft rocks in the wilderness,
and gave them drink in abundance.
You made streams flow out of the rock,
you caused the waters to tumble like rivers.
But for all this they sinned against you,
and rebelled against their God in the desert.   *Refrain*

They wilfully put you to the test,
and demanded food for their appetite.
They spoke against you and said,
"Can you prepare a table in the wilderness?
You indeed struck the rock and the waters flowed,
but can you also give bread and meat for your people?"
When you heard it you were angry
and a fire was kindled against Jacob,
your wrath blazing against Israel.
For they put no trust in you,
nor would they believe your power to save.
Then you commanded the clouds above,
and opened the doors of heaven.
You rained down manna for them to eat,
and gave them the bread of heaven.
Mere mortals ate the food of angels,
which you gave to them in abundance.
You stirred up the south east wind
and guided it by your power.

Refrain: Deluded, rebellious, estranged,
we know neither ourselves nor our God,
the God whose ways are mysterious,
an enigma, a question, a riddle.

You rained down meat on them thick as dust,
and winged birds like the sands of the sea.
You made them fall into the midst of their camp,
and all about their tents.
So they ate and were well filled,
for you had given them what they desired.
But before they had satisfied their craving,
while the food was still in their mouths,
your anger blazed up against them
and you slew their strongest men
and laid low the youth of Israel. *Refrain*

But for all this they sinned yet more
and put no faith in your wonders.
So you ended their days like a breath,
and their years with sudden terror.
When you struck them down then they sought you,
they turned and searched eagerly for their God.
They remembered that God was their rock,
their strength and their redeemer.
But they lied to you with their mouths,
and dissembled with their tongues,
for their hearts were not fixed upon you,
nor were they true to your covenant.
Yet being merciful you forgave their iniquity,
and withheld your hand from destroying them.
Many times you turned your anger aside
and would not wholly arouse your fury.
You remembered that they were but flesh,
like a wind that passes and does not return. *Refrain*

How often they grieved you in the wilderness,
and rebelled against you in the desert.
Again and again they put you to the test
and provoked you, O Holy One of Israel.

They did not remember your power,
or the day when you rescued them,
how you wrought your signs in Egypt,
your wonders in the country of Zoan.
For you turned their rivers into blood,
so that they could not drink from the streams.
You sent swarms of flies that devoured them,
and frogs that laid them waste.
You gave their crops to the locust,
and the fruits of their labours to the grasshopper.
You struck down their vines with hailstones,
and their sycamore trees with frost.
You gave up their cattle to the hail,
and their flocks to the flash of the lightning.
You loosed on them a terrible anger,
a fierce indignation, your distress and your fury.
You would not spare them from death
but gave up their lives to the pestilence.
You struck down the firstborn of Egypt,
the firstfruits of the womb in the dwelling of Ham.

Refrain

As for your own people you led them out like sheep,
and guided them in the wilderness like a flock.
You led them to safety and they were not afraid,
but the sea overwhelmed their enemies.
You brought them to the land of the promise,
to the mountains your right hand had won.
You drove out the tribes before you
and gave their lands to your people.
You settled the tribes of Israel in their tents.
But they rebelled against you, O God of deliverance,
and put you to the test:
they would not obey your Commandments.
They turned back and were treacherous again,
they turned aside, slack as an unstrung bow.
They provoked you to anger at heathen shrines,
moved you to jealousy with their carved idols.

Refrain: Deluded, rebellious, estranged,
we know neither ourselves nor our God,
the God whose ways are mysterious,
an enigma, a question, a riddle.

You heard and were angry, you utterly rejected them,
you forsook the tabernacle at Shiloh,
the tent where you dwelt among the people.
You gave the ark of your power into captivity,
your glory into the hands of the enemy.
You delivered your people to the sword,
and were enraged against them.
Fire devoured the young men,
there was no one to bewail the young women,
Their priests fell by the sword,
and there was none to mourn for the widows.   *Refrain*

Then, O God, you awoke from sleep,
like a warrior inflamed with wine.
You struck the backsides of your enemies,
bringing them down to their shame.
You rejected the family of Joseph,
you refused the tribe of Ephraim.
But you chose the tribe of Judah,
and the hill of Zion which you loved.
You built the sanctuary high as the heavens,
and as firm as the earth which you founded.
You chose David the youngest as your servant,
and plucked him away from the sheepfold.
You took him from guiding the flocks,
to be the shepherd of your people Jacob,
and of Israel your own possession.
He tended them with a true and faithful heart,
and guided them with skilful hands.   *Refrain*

And so the story unfolded,
the mystery ever deepening,
a kingdom split apart,
a people carried off into exile.
Even the clue of the Cross
has left us many a puzzle.
Our loyalty ebbs and flows,
our sense of your presence too.
Those in high office betray you,
integrity crumbles in gossip.
The obscure are so often submerged,
the powerful far beyond love.
The stones of the churches decay,
your agelong Spirit moves on.
We have become so timid and fearful,
we refuse to enter the unknown.
We desperately cling to our comforts,
one by one you take them away.
We resent you stripping us bare,
untrusting of this prelude to glory.   *Refrain*

Mysterious God, choosing the small, the unnoticed, the obscure, to renew the way of your covenant when your followers wander and fail you, strive yet with our intractable clay; open us to the love you revealed to us in Jesus Christ, emptied of power, untouched by illusion, dying unrecognized, yet for those with eyes to see the decisive clue to the mystery of your being.

THE BODY OF GOD

Refrain: O God, we wound your body:
         come quickly, heal and save us.

We neglect, we ravage the body.
We rape the earth, your temple.
We pollute the rivers, the oceans.
We care not for the soil that sustains us.
And the earth cries out in pain.
The algae fills the creeks,
sucking down the unwary,
releasing its poisonous fumes.

We neglect, we ravage the body.
We take our pleasures with violence.
We forget the language of reverence.
We care not for the weak and the vulnerable.
And the people cry out in pain.
Their anger rises in vengeance:
they pass on the needles infected,
they delight in spreading disease.

We neglect, we ravage the body.
We flatten the beautiful cities.
We ransack the places of prayer.
We care not for beauty, for peace.
And the land cries out in pain.
The contorted ruins smoulder.
The survivors stumble in shock,
their children inherit their wounds.

We neglect, we ravage the body.
Radiation drifts on the wind.
Waste is dumped in the oceans.
We care not for fish or for bird.
And the trees cry out in pain,
sprouting mis-shapen leaves.
An earthquake in the depths of the seas
splits open the canisters of doom.

O God, forgive our murderous deeds and blind, unthinking rage. Give us your Spirit of compassionate anger, that we may live and work in harmony with you for the healing of the body of this planet, gasping for air, sores weeping on its skin. Make us a people of one earth, loved and cherished as bodies should.

THE FACE OF GOD

Refrain: Light of the Spirit shine on us;
Face of Glory transfigure us;
Eyes of Christ restore us.

Radiant and glorious God,
shining through the universe,
lighting our tortuous landscape,
guiding your troublesome peoples,
straighten the path of your coming,
stride forth to meet us and save us.

Radiant and glorious God,
shining through a human face,
illuminate our blinded eyes,
guide us with an inner light,
feed us who gasp by the wayside,
lift us up with nurturing hand.

We have misused the freedom you gave us,
we have felt the anger of your love.
You have fed us with the bread of tears,
and given us many a bitter drink.

You cared for us like a young vine,
clearing the ground and planting us in.
You nourished the soil for our roots to deepen,
you sent us the warmth of the sun and the rain.
We flourished and grew strong,
our boughs were like those of the cedar.
Our branches stretched out to the sea,
our tender shoots to the great river.

Why then have you sent us drought?
Why do the locusts devour our fruit?
Why does the wind tear our branches?
Why do the boars of the forest uproot us?
O God, no longer do we see your face,
no longer do we hear your voice.

With the eye of your compassion look upon us.
Prune us if need be, but do not destroy.
We are a fickle and cowardly people:
strengthen our wills and heal our wounds.
Let all that is wilful in us perish at your word,
let all that is slothful be burned.
Empower us again to follow your way,
give us life and we shall delight in your name.

Living God, whose face no one can look upon and live, sustain our faith in the human face of Christ revealing the infinite depths of your justice and compassion. So shine upon us with the light of your Spirit that we may recognize you in the faces of one another and realize the presence of your glory among us.

THE GOD WHO YEARNS TO SAVE

*Refrain: O God who saved a small people
from slavery, oppression, and fear,
deliver the peoples of earth
from our imprisonments one of another.*

The people of God sang for joy,
the people of the God of Jacob.
They beat the drum,
they plucked the strings,
they blew the horn of the ram,
and the people gathered.
At the phases of the moon
they held their festival,
even as their ancestors
from their time in Egypt.

God spoke to the people in a voice not known:
I eased your shoulders of burdens,
your hands were freed from the load.
You called to me and I rescued you,
I answered from the place of secret thunder,
I tested you at the waters of Meribah.

My people, listen to my charge.
Israel, if only you would hear me!
Do not bow down to alien gods,
let there be no strange gods among you.
I am your God and your Saviour,
who brought you out of the land of Egypt.
Open your mouth wide and I will satisfy you:
filled with my presence you will live in my truth.

But you would not listen to my voice,
you would have nothing to do with me.
So I gave you up to your stubborn hearts,
to walk according to your own designs.
If only you would listen to me,
if only you would walk in my ways.
I would soon defeat your enemies,
and lift you free of your oppressors.
Those who despise me would cringe before me,
they would be trapped in their fate for ever.
But I would feed you with the finest wheat,
with honey from the rock I would satisfy you.

Like our ancestors, O God, we would worship you,
we would be glad and sing for joy.
To us as to them you would speak,
reminding us of your yearning and care.
In the moment of prayer we are one with them,
our past is alive and so is the future.
You would warn and admonish us still,
for we also wander from your way.
We lay burdens upon one another:
oppressed, we oppress in our turn.
Spring the traps we have laid,
deliver us from the compulsion to punish.
Do not imprison us for ever,
even those we see as our enemies.

Do not exalt us who are far from deserving it,
at the expense of hell for our enemies.
The people of earth are your people now.
Work in us all your deeds of deliverance,
even in those who abuse and enslave,
in those who traffic in terror or drugs,
in those who dictate the slaughter of innocents.
If they are so thoroughly wicked,
that they dissolve into dust at your sight,
so let it be, your design come to nothing.
But would not your love then have failed?
Inscrutable God, is that not so?

Dear God, your heart yearns with longing for us to realize how trapped we are. You give us the freedom to choose to be imprisoned for ever. Yet your love with insistence compels. Turn our hearts and wills without our knowing it, and kindle in us the desire for true freedom. Deliver us in love's most costly way, and give us the courage to bear it, in Jesus, for whom such love was the weight of glory.

THE IDLE PROMISES OF IDOLS

Refrain: Down to the dust, vain idols!
Come, living God of justice.

They seem to be as gods,
those who promise utopias.
Fickle as a crowd we gawp,
cheering the latest idolatry:
Romantic illusions of singers,
false pledges of politicians,
slippery words of the gurus,
sleek suits of the televangelists.

From your pedestals you no longer see,
high above the weak and oppressed.
You say nothing about the orphaned and widowed,
never touch the lives of the silenced.
You say nothing of the toughness of love,
you promise no just laws for the poor,
your words pass over the stricken,
your mouthings stir up irrational guilt.

You proclaim a false god of terror,
by threats you hold on to your power,
you never show the true God,
wounded by love, embracing the failure.
Indeed you are lost, you crumble,
you wander about in the darkness,
you stumble, you do not understand,
your name will vanish into dust.

O God, make your promises true,
imbue us with your Spirit of justice.
Favour the oppressed, humble the oppressor,
bring laughter and love to our eyes.

O God, living God, if you are the living God, justify your ways to your people, and let not our cry for justice echo in silence. We cling to our trust in your promises. Fulfil them. Do not betray us. Do not be to us a false god.

THE ENEMIES OF GOD

Refrain: Redeem your enemies, O God,
those who misuse your power.
Transform us all by your presence,
a power made holy by love.

A small people, in a small land,
surrounded by tribes that were hostile,
threatened by empires expanding,
cried out to their God to protect them.
Their enemies made their alliances,
whispering, conspiring, plotting together.
They schemed against those whom God cherished,
they seized on the pastures of God.

Who are your enemies now, O God?
A people apathetic who do not care,
those who sit at ease while millions slave,
those who eat their fill while children starve.
And those who wage war in the name of their God,
and those who supply them with weapons;
those who poison the rivers and seas,
and those who spread lies through our minds.

Destroy them, O God, who poison the land,
let their remains become dung for the earth.
Make them like chaff before the wind,
as insubstantial as thistledown.
May they cower backwards in fear,
flattened by the fury of your wind,
shrivelled by the heat of your fire,
the flame that sets hillsides ablaze.
Let them be disgraced and dismayed for ever,
and those who collude – like ourselves.
Wild-eyed, bewildered, let us tremble,
in a moment of dread and of truth.

Refrain: Redeem your enemies, O God,
those who misuse your power.
Transform us all by your presence,
a power made holy by love.

Yes, we yearn for the omnipotent king,
the ruler who gives life to the people,
who leads out his armies to lay waste and destroy.
Such a king was an ikon of God,
but the King on a Cross shows a power that is humbling,
an awesome love that endures through the pain,
that takes our rage and our venom to heart,
all of us guilty together.

May we turn from our hatreds and face you,
burned clean by the eye of your love,
that you may forgive our destruction and greed,
and our naming of strangers as enemies.
In your Spirit let us care for the earth,
in compassion one for another.
Let us welcome the strangers and share what we have,
enjoying the wealth of justice and friendship.

O God, ease our paranoia from our hearts, grown cold in this time of fear.
Remind us of the truth that even those who terrify us — eyes harsh and
vengeful — are created and loved by you. Show us how to be reconciled and
so to live in peace.

ON PILGRIMAGE

Refrain: The end is known in the midst of the journey:
the fulfilment is beyond our imagining.

How lovely are your dwellings, O God,
how beautiful are the holy places.
In the days of my pilgrimage I yearn for them:
they are the temples of your living presence.
I have a desire and longing to enter my true home:
my heart and my flesh rejoice in the living God.

For the sparrow has found a house for herself,
and the swallow a nest to lay her young.
Even so are those who dwell in your house –
they will always be praising you.
And your Spirit makes a home deep within us:
let us welcome and delight in your Presence.

Blessed are those whose strength is in you,
in whose heart are your ways,
who trudging through the plains of misery
find in them an unexpected spring,
a well from deep below the barren ground,
and the pools are filled with water.

They become springs of healing for others,
reservoirs of compassion to those who are bruised.
Strengthened themselves they lend courage to others,
and God will be there at the end of their journey.

O God of our ancestors, hear my prayer:
guide me as you did your servants of old.
Bless those who govern on the people's behalf,
keep us close to your will and your ways.

*Refrain: The end is known in the midst of the journey:
            the fulfilment is beyond our imagining.*

One day lived in your presence
is better than a thousand in my own dwelling.
I had rather beg in the burning sun
on the threshold of the house of my God
than sit in cool courtyards
of luxury and worldly success.

For you are my light and my shield,
you will give me your grace and your glory.
You are ready with bountiful gifts,
overflowing to those who follow you.

Living God of love,
blessed are those who put their trust in you.

*O God of the desert pilgrims, we who are wearied by monotonous days in
the sun, who are battered by the monstrous whirling winds, surprise us yet
with a monstrance of wonder, a revelation of love, an oasis of refreshment,
a taste of the harvest, a moment of grace.*

ROOTED IN ONE LAND?

Refrain: May we cherish the land of our birth,
and be rooted in the Earth and in God.

We thank you, O God, for the land of our birth,
for a country to cherish and honour,
for farms and cities to care for,
gardens and houses to dwell in.

You chose a particular people,
you gave land to a wandering tribe,
that they might learn to follow your way,
and give light to the nations around them.

So often that light was dimmed by their sin,
as they turned aside from your path.
You led them through the mourning of exile,
and they knew you as Lord of the Earth.

Then you filled the life of one particular man,
born of your people, brought up in that land,
whose name has spread all over the earth,
calling us all to be neighbours.

Still does your love strive with our waywardness,
reaching across the abyss that is wrath,
opening our eyes to the needs of the hidden ones,
compelling us to cherish an earth that is fragile.

We look upon the world and its peoples,
and there seem few grounds for our faith.
We turn our hearts towards the Ground of our being,
and you meet us with riches of grace.

So you give us life yet again,
and we your people sing and rejoice,
speaking your praise on behalf of the creatures,
claiming our inheritance as stewards of Earth.

Refrain: May we cherish the land of our birth,
and be rooted in the Earth and in God.

Indeed you will speak peace to your people,
to your faithful ones who have turned their hearts.
Truly your salvation is near those who fear you,
and your glory will shine on our earth.

Mercy and truth have met together,
righteousness and peace have kissed each other.
Faithfulness will spring up from the earth,
and justice leap to meet it from heaven.

O God, you will give us all that is good,
and our lands will yield their plenty.
For righteousness will go before you,
and clear the way for your appearing.

God of the whole earth and God of each land, so guide us in your Spirit that
we may not betray our country for the sake of fanatical ideals, nor betray our
earth out of fearful and blinkered loyalties, through Jesus Christ the Just.

GOD IS GOD

*Refrain: Persistent in faithfulness,
constant in love.*

Like the sun through the heavens,
and the moon through its phases,
like the rivers that flow,
and the seas that welcome them,
so are you, God of the universe,

Like the humble of heart,
and the kindly of soul,
like the ones who forgive
and are no longer bitter,
so are you, God of compassion,

You hear the cry of the afflicted,
you listen to the howl of the lonely,
you continually search for the lost,
you heal the hurts of the wounded,
for you are a God of yearning,

You gladden the human heart,
you lift the burdens of the depressed,
you give new hope to the despairing,
you reach to the depths of the grave,
for you are a God of rejoicing,

You bind the rebellious,
you quieten the strident,
you draw the fangs of the ruthless,
you silence the bullying dictators,
for you are a God of justice,

OMIT

You welcome the stranger,
you embrace the outcast,
you bear our pain,
you strive with our evil,
for you are a God crucified and risen,

Refrain: Persistent in faithfulness,
constant in love.

Abiding is your love,
enduring is your patience,
everlasting are your truths,
eternal, is your glory,
O God, you are God.

God of mystery and revelation, at the extremes of our distress and despair,
when you are the only hope left, let us hear your name again, and so take
courage on the journey:

I Am Who I Am,
I Shall Be Who I Shall Be,
That Which I Am I Shall Be,
That Which I Shall Be I Am.

I shall be there as the one who I there shall be,
I am with you always as I always choose to be with you.

I shall be there in the encounter
you cannot predict,
but there you will meet me,
and I shall be for you
as the one who there shall be.

CITIES OF PILGRIMAGE

Refrain: Lured by the God whose greatness is Love,
we draw near to the gates of the City.

Egypt, the old enslaver,
Babylon, the ancient foe,
Philistines over the border,
Phoenicians from the shores of the sea,
Ethiopians from over the mountains,
those who once were our enemies
now worship God in Jerusalem.

The eye of faith looks to the dawn,
to the day of peace universal,
to a new age of the salvation of God,
to an earth transfigured, made new.
The dancers dance; the singers make melody;
the fountains of God enliven the City.

The peoples are widely scattered
over the earth and across the sea.
A poet with vision broods
as the pilgrims draw near to Jerusalem,
to the God who draws them together
to give praise on the holy mountain.

The peoples of another time,
citizens of far-flung cities,
the powerful of Washington,
of Moscow and Beijing,
the weak of Sao Paulo,
of Soweto and Calcutta,
all the peoples give you praise.

*Refrain: Lured by the God whose greatness is Love,
          we draw near to the gates of the city.*

Pilgrims to Jerusalem,
to Mecca and to Rome:
Faithful of Canterbury,
of Geneva and Byzantium:
Gatherers to the rivers,
to the Naranjara and the Ganges:
Markers of the journey
through the deserts and the mountains:
they celebrate in gratitude,
in wonder and rejoicing.

No room for the aloof and arrogant,
for the divisive and superior spirit:
God is greater than the idols of nations,
deeper in mystery than any faith.
Like a people of old, small, obscure,
stretched beyond fear to a wider belief,
so are God's people today
challenged by a love that is awesome,
drawn to the gates of the city of God,
whose name is yet to be known.

*Living God, greater than the human heart, greater than all the peoples of the
world, greater than the faiths that try to cage you, shatter the idols which we
make to keep us safe, to claim you for ourselves, to portray you in superior
ways. Humble us, living God, and draw us by the magnet of your Love into
the glory of your Presence and the harmony of a new Jerusalem.*

IN BLEAK DESPAIR

*Refrain: There is drought in the depths of my being,
no rain, no water, no life.*

The praise of your salvation, O God,
has died on lips that are parched.
The story of your wonders towards us
has turned hollow, bitter, and sour.
I doubt any prayer can enter your heart,
your ear is deaf to my cry.

Soul-deep I am full of troubles,
and my life draws near to the grave.
I totter on the edge of the abyss,
ghostly, ghastly, shrivelled.
I am like the wounded in war that stagger,
like a corpse strewn out on the battlefield.

I belong no more to my people,
I am cut off from your presence, O God.
You have put me in the lowest of dungeons,
in a pit of scurrying rats.
To a wall that drips with water I am chained,
my feet sink into mud.

I feel nothing but your pounding in my head,
surges of pain overwhelm me.
I cannot endure this suffering,
this furious onslaught, so searing.
I can remember no time without terror,
without turmoil and trouble of mind.

I have been dying since the day of my birth:
O God, have I ever really existed?
I have never known who I am,
and even my friends who once loved me,
who gave me some sense of belonging,
have drawn back in horror and left me.

*Refrain: There is drought in the depths of my being,
no rain, no water, no life.*

My sight fails me because of my trouble;
there is no light in the place of deep dark.
I am alone, bewildered, and lost;
yet I cannot abandon you, God.
Day after day I cry out to you,
early in the morning I pray in your absence.

Do you work wonders among the tombs?
Shall the dead rise up and praise you?
Will your lovingkindness reach to the grave,
your faithfulness to the place of destruction?
Are the stories of old an illusion?
Will you again do what is right in the land?

*In times of despair, O God, rain showers of gentleness upon us, that we may
be kindly one to another and also to ourselves. Renew in us the spirit of hope.
Even in the depths of the darkness, may we hear the approach of the One who
harrows hell and greets even Judas with a kiss.*

THE PROMISE

Refrain: The promises of God stand for ever:
when will we see them fulfilled?

We cannot know the depths of your being, O God,
you are to us a mystery profound.
Revealed as a love that is selfless,
still do we touch but a fringe of your being.
Your promises of love are steady and sure,
and yet in perplexity we doubt them.

Your people of old called you king of high heaven:
they thought of you praised by the holy ones,
by the inner council who held you in awe,
who praised your wonders and deeds.
They bowed down to the king who was just,
whose promises were very sure.
Justice was the foundation of your reign,
lovingkindness and faithfulness your closest attendants.

They praised you as the God of Power:
no-one could stand in the way of your purpose.
In strength and faithfulness and glory
you ruled the powers of creation.
You stilled the surging of the sea,
you reined in the monsters of chaos.
When the floods drowned out our wickedness,
you promised to withhold your destruction.

Your promises reached out to a particular people,
you gave them a land of their own.
You rescued them from slavery in Egypt,
and brought them safe through the wilderness.
With joy they shouted in triumph,
and walked in the light of your countenance.
You were their glory and strength,
their heads lifted high by your favour.

Refrain: The promises of God stand for ever:
when will we see them fulfilled?

You made a covenant with David your servant,
you gave him a promise to be with him for ever,
to establish his house and his throne,
to build it up for all generations.
You chose a mere youth, no warrior,
the youngest of brothers, not the eldest.
You promised to scatter his enemies,
to enlarge the bounds of his kingdom.
He called to you as his father,
his God, and the rock of his salvation.
You made him your firstborn son,
highest among the rulers of earth.

When he wandered away from your path,
when his children forsook your law,
you punished their rebellion,
you gave strength to their enemies.
And yet you betrayed not your faithfulness,
you did not profane your covenant.
Once and for all you swore by your holiness,
that you would not prove false to David.

Yet it seemed as if the promise lay shattered;
in your wrath you rejected your anointed.
You spurned the covenant with your servant,
you defiled his crown to the dust.
You broke down the walls of the city,
you made his strongholds desolate.
The scavengers swooped down to plunder,
the king was scorned by his neighbours.
You exalted the power of his enemies,
and gladdened their mocking hearts.
His bright sword lay tarnished and broken,
no longer shall he stand in the battle.
You brought his glory to an end,
you have cast down his throne to the ground.

For centuries the seed of the promise was buried,
unnoticed in the sands of the desert.
Yet human hearts cherished the hope,
waiting and yearning through oppression and exile.
At last you spoke to the young and the humble,
Mary responded to the grace of your Word.
The carpenter Joseph accepted the dream,
and the promise to David burst into life.

Your Spirit seized the being of Jesus,
anointing him in grace and in power.
The poor heard the news of acceptance and love,
the bolts of the prisoners slid back.
The blind recovered their sight,
the wounds of the victims were healed.
But the challenge of the promise was too great:
they draw back from love's fierce demands.
The incarnate of God was left quite alone,
the promise broken on the wood of the cross.

From the ashes of despair a phoenix arose,
from death's very tombs is the promise fulfilled.
The women who went to care for a corpse
were surprised with terror and joy.
Your Spirit, risen Christ, leaped through the land,
the flame that gives warmth and light to our hearts.

They expected soon your return,
that the day of your glory would dawn.
Yet again did their hopes fade away,
and the centuries began to roll by.
The promise was obscured by worldly success,
the corruptions of power, the slither of compromise.
The sufferings of children still cry aloud,
terror and greed freeze the heart still.

O God of the Promise, but fleetingly fulfilled among us, test us not beyond our endurance, keep hope alive, renew in us the Spirit of the risen Christ, nourish among us the firstfruits of your harvest, and hasten the day when we shall know the Promise has been kept.

TIME AND ETERNITY

Refrain: Admist the confusions of time,
may we hear eternity's heartbeat.

God of eternity,
God beyond time,
our refuge and hope
from one generation to another:
Before the mountains rose from the sea,
before the rivers carved the valleys,
before time itself began,
you are God, eternal.

From dust we came,
to dust we return.
"Be shaped from the clay,
be crumbled to earth."
Creator of life, of death,
so did you order our ways.
A thousand years in your sight
are as yesterday.
As a watch in the night
comes quickly to an end,
so the years pass before you,
in a flicker of the eye.

The years are like the grass,
which in the morning is green,
and by evening is dried up and withered.
As the grass shrivels in the smoke,
so is our pride consumed in your fire:
we are afraid of the burning of the dross.

All our misdeeds and deceits
are brought to light before your eyes,
all our secret sins
made clear in the light of your truth.
When you are angry,
our days are as nothing:
our years come to an end,
vanishing with a sigh.

The decades soon pass,
no more than a handful.
Some show vigour in age,
yet even they are soon gone.
So much of our span is wearisome,
full of labour and sorrow.

O the speed of it all,
and the vanity of the years:
all I have done is like straw,
and most of it forgotten already.
Success crumbles into dust:
there is nothing to pay love's account.

Who is even aware
of the purging of your wrath?
Who pays a moment's attention
to the fierceness of your love?
Teach us to number our days,
and apply our hearts to wisdom.

Turn again, O God, do not delay:
give grace to your servants.
Satisfy us in the morning
with your lovingkindness.
So we shall rejoice and be glad
all the days of our life.

Give us days of gladness
to make up for those of affliction,
for the years of adversity.
Show your servants your deeds,
and your glory to our children.
May your grace be upon us:
fill us with the Spirit of love.
For in the evening of our days
when we come to be judged,
we shall be known only by love,
delivered only by love.

Eternal God, thank you for your gift of time and the measure death gives to our days. They pass so quickly as to dent our pride. May we neither rely on our achievements nor be downcast at our failures. Keep us but faithful to your love, and dependent on your grace alone. We ask this in the Spirit of the One who died a human failure, and died so young.

UNSHAKEABLE TRUST IN GOD

*Refrain: You are trustworthy and true, my God,
holding fast to your covenant of love.*

At nightfall I come to an inn on my journey,
a place of refuge, of your presence, O God,
a sanctuary, a temple, the tent of your dwelling,
where I lie down to sleep in safety.
Under the shade of your hovering wings
I have no fear of the unknown in the dark.

You have set me free from the snare of the hunter,
from the depths of the pit of snakes.
My trust in you keeps me from terror,
they sense no need to attack me.
You overshadow me with your wings,
I am safe under your feathers.
As a mother protects her brood,
so are you tender and strong towards me.
With your faithfulness as shield and defence,
I have courage to face any danger.

In the dead of night I have no terror to fear,
neither dread in the daytime the plunge of the dagger,
nor fear the plague that stalks in the darkness,
nor the fever that strikes in the heat of the day.
Though a thousand fall beside me in battle,
ten thousand at my right hand,
even though faith has endured to the limit,
still do I reach to the God who saves.

Yes, with a faith that moves mountains
still do I trust in my God.
I shall never know lasting harm,
whatever the testing ordeal.
With my own eyes I shall see
your judgment and mercy, O God.

Refrain: You are trustworthy and true, my God,
holding fast to your covenant of love.

Because I have said,
"O God, you are my hope:
you are my refuge and stronghold,"
no great evil will overwhelm me,
no final destruction crush me.
For you will command your angels
to keep me in your narrow ways:
they will bear me up in their hands
lest I dash my foot against a stone.
I may step upon cobra and adder,
but even the snakes I shall tread underfoot.
In the strength of my God,
in impossible faith,
I will bind the powers that rebel.

"Because I am bound to you in love,
therefore I will deliver you.
I will lift you out of danger
because you hold on to my name.
You know me in intimate trust,
in your inner heart you are loyal and true.
In your anguish and need I am with you,
I will set you free and clothe you with glory.
You will live to be full of years,
you will know the abundance of my salvation."

Open our eyes, O God of marvellous wonder, beyond the puzzling reflections
in the mirror, beyond the brutal images of violence, beyond the fading of the
years, that we may see the wide open spaces of promised freedom, may
glimpse the communion of saints and brush the wings of angels, may
recognize for a moment the glory of the universe, where darkness and doubt
dissolve, where the gash of the wound shines, where death and destruction
have vanished for ever.

THE STEADINESS OF GOD

Refrain: Steady and sure is the pulse of your heart,
quietening all our distress.

How precious a thing it is
to give thanks to you, O God.
How good and beautiful
to sing your name, most beloved,
to receive your love in our hearts
at the rising of the sun in the morning,
to sing of your faithfulness
in the watches of the night,
on the strings of the harp and the lyre.

In everything you have done you make me glad,
I sing for joy at the beauty of creation.
The depths of your thoughts I cannot comprehend,
the wonder of the universe I shall never fathom.
Everything that happens impinges on your heart,
in wisdom and love you hold us and heal us.
The wounds of the broken-hearted you bind,
you patiently stitch the severed limbs of your body.

The brutal do not understand your ways,
the cruel add to the pain that you suffer.
Because of the freedom you give us,
wickedness can sprout like the grass in the spring.
But in the drought of summer those who do evil
in their need have no one to turn to.
Cut off from the flow of companionship
they wither, decay, and die.
The fruits of their wrongdoing shrivel,
burnt up in the heat of your fire.

*Refrain: Steady and sure is the pulse of your heart,
quietening all our distress.*

Those who have rebelled against you
will scatter their arms as they flee.
Lost and bewildered they will cower in fear,
at the mercy of those they betrayed,
whose eyes now look down on their enemies,
whose ears hear the crash of their fall.

Yet the oppressed draw near in compassion,
with water to slake their enemies' thirst.
Their deeds are as perfume so fragrant,
a precious oil with which you anoint them.
With their quiet and dignified presence
they will shame their enemies to silence.
Vibrant with life, they will invite them to dance,
their eyes glistening with laughter and joy.

Those who keep faith will flourish like the palm tree,
like the spreading cedar of Lebanon.
Planted firm in the earth of your courtyard, O God,
they will mature and give fruit for your house.
To old age they will be vigorous and fresh,
sturdy and laden with branches.
Like the trees and the mountains strong,
they will confirm your patient endurance.

*God of infinite pains and patience, in these our turbulent days take from us
the stress of seeking for security in force of arms and luxury of comfort, and
give us the quiet confidence of those who have enough for today and who trust
you for tomorrow.*

A CALM AUTHORITY

Refrain: To the chaos that storms, without and within,
speak with assurance, Peace, be still.

In the silence of the night your word was spoken,
a calm creative word in the heavens.
It was but a whisper of your voice,
the faint rustling of your robes of glory.
Sovereign of the universe, yet did you hide yourself,
so that your light might not shrivel us.

In quiet ways you hold the world together,
chaos contained by your compassionate power.
When the seas hurl their pounding waves,
when the hurricane howls across the ocean.
when the tornado rips through the farmland,
when the rivers rage through city streets,
still do you set a limit to their power,
that they may not overwhelm us for ever.

The surges of chaos pound through our heads,
a murderous fury rises within us;
wrenched apart by the sobbing of grief,
we are lost and bewildered, tossed to and fro.
A relentless pain throbs through our bones,
we scream in the night at the faces of terror.
Yet even as we plunge in the fearful abyss,
the face of the crucified is there in the void.

For where do we best see your power?
Nowhere else but a man who is stricken,
deserted and betrayed by his friends,
killed by his people, an outcast, unclean.
The chaos they dared not face in themselves
they hurled with abuse and the nails.
They hid from their pain in the thicket of laws,
and refused to allow their wounds to be healed.
They defended themselves in self-righteous armour,
and refused the calm word of forgiveness and love.

*Refrain: To the chaos that storms, without and within,
            speak with assurance, Peace, be still.*

The material world looked so solid around us,
we never even dreamed of the chaos in matter.
As the cloud mushroomed high in the desert,
we were stunned by the force we'd unleashed.
The power of apocalypse is now in our hands:
is the calm word of God lost for ever?

*Creator God, you have entered the very fabric of the universe, for ever
committed to bringing harmony out of chaos. Assure us of your presence in
the midst of our perplexities and fears, that you will endure with us and
speak the calm word of a deeper and more lasting peace.*

THAT JUSTICE BE DONE

Refrain: *Hungry for mercy,*
         thirsty for justice,
         fierce is our cry:
         Put right what is wrong.

A child is murdered in the street,
a widow is mugged for a meagre purse,
a stone shatters the bedroom window
of a couple whose skin is strange.
A violent spirit runs amok,
and the powerless are the first to suffer.

Masked gunman, why do you kill?
Arrogant fool, why do you trample?
Drunken gang, why have your hearts
become the very stones that you throw?
What is this rampaging spirit
that sweeps the mob to such fury?

No wonder the widower weeps,
no wonder the mother howls.
No wonder they shrink back in fear
or cry, Revenge, through broken glass.
O God, stop these horrors of our every day,
this wasteland of our killing fields.

How long will the ways of violence triumph?
How long will cruel words pierce the air?
How long will the arrogant boast of their conquests?
How long will prejudice keep us apart?
O God, do you not hear, do you not see?
Will you not chasten? Where is your justice?

Arise, Judge of all the earth.
May your justice be seen to be done.
Lift the burdens of oppression,
heal the crushed in mind and spirit,
bind up the wounds of the injured,
bend the necks that are stiffened with pride.

Refrain: Hungry for mercy,
thirsty for justice,
fierce is our cry:
Put right what is wrong.

You know the thoughts of all our hearts,
you know that each of us is no more than a breath.
Yet you will not cast us away, people of the earth,
you will not forsake those you have created.
Justice will be seen to flourish again,
vindicating those who are true of heart.

Take up the cause of the weak and helpless,
speak for those overpowered by words,
bring to light the corruptions of justice,
bind those who spread evil by means of the law,
expose the conspiracies of silence,
let not the innocent be condemned.

If you had not been our helper,
we should have lost our way in the mists.
When our feet slipped on the narrow path
you held us firm in your merciful strength.
In all the anxieties of our minds
your peace steadied and calmed us.
In all the doubtings of our hearts
your presence sustained and consoled us.

Humble those who work evil,
silence those whose words weave corruption.
Gently withdraw the sting of their violence:
with healing ointment may their poison dissolve.
Remove the power of those who wreak havoc,
put them to tasks of service and care.

In your good time bring us face to face,
oppressors and victims who often collude.
None of us has words of defence in your presence,
we are silenced by the power of your truth and your love.
May the victims among us stretch out our hands
to touch those who would now shrink away,
gently to turn their faces towards us,
that our eyes may fill with mercy and wonder.

So may we look with confidence towards you,
loving God, so awesome in mercy,
fierce in compassion and judgment,
yearning for reconciliation and peace,
bearing the pain with a heartfelt cry,
in which grief and joy become one.

Spirit of the living God, in communion with you and with the cries of those who suffer injustice, work in and through us new deeds of discerning wisdom and true judgment, that we may know among us the fulfilment of your promises, even the firstfruits of your reign of justice.

ENCOUNTERING THE REDEEMING CREATOR

Refrain: Let us sing to the One who is creating us,
let us renew our covenant with God.

Let us sing to the God who is creating us,
let us rejoice in the Rock of of our salvation.

Dear God, we celebrate your presence with thanksgiving,
and with our whole heart sing psalms of praise.
We greet you with love, Creator of the universe,
Spirit who strives with the chaos of the world.
With your finger you shape the mountains of the earth,
and the depths of the valleys are scoured by your power.
The wings of your Spirit brood over the seas,
and your hands mould the dry land.

Not one of the threatening powers escapes you,
the thundering of the gods on the cloud-capped mountains,
the rumbling of demons as the earth quakes,
the faces that loom in the dreams of the night,
the punishing voices from our helpless past.
The power of your love reaches so far
that nothing and no-one is beyond your redemption.

O come let us worship and lift our hearts high
and adore our God, our Creator.
For you indeed are God, and we are your people,
crafted by the skill of your hands.

"Listen to my voice this day
and harden not your hearts.
Do not be like your ancestors
who saw the great deeds I had done,
yet put me to the test in the desert,
at the place of Bitterness and Quarrel.

"They were wayward in their hearts,
they were ignorant of my ways.
So they could sense but the wrath of my love,
and were condemned to a restless wandering."

If we listen to your voice deep within us,
we shall know the mercy and grace of your love.
We shall see you as Judge of the earth,
doing right in the sight of all peoples,
judging us all in your faithfulness,
quelling our rebellious strife.

Spirit of Christ, take shape among us,
Spirit of the One who fulfilled God's promise.
Humble us in awe at your presence:
let us adore you in the silence of love.
Deepen our gratitude in obedience and trust,
in your covenant made sure for ever.

To the beauty and bounty of your creation and grace, we have responded, O God, with desecration and greed. We have presumed upon the constant renewal of your gifts. Give us penitent hearts and the will to cherish the earth, that we may know you again as our redeeming Creator, bringing good from our wastes and sorrows.

JOY IN GOD

Refrain: Sing to the great God a new song,
sing to the Creator, sing the whole earth.
Let nature and peoples join in harmony
to sing praise to the God of glory.

We sing to you, God, and praise your name,
telling of your salvation from day to day,
declaring your glory to those who do not know you,
and your wonders to the peoples of the earth.
Marvellous God, you are greatly to be praised,
more to be honoured than all the powers.
Glory and worship are before you,
power and honour are in your sanctuary.

May we, the household of your people,
ascribe to you worship and glory,
giving you the honour due to your name,
bringing presents as we come into your house.
We worship you in the beauty of holiness:
let the whole earth stand in awe of you.
Let us tell it out among the peoples that you are God,
and that you are making the round world so sure,
held within the bounds of your love,
and that you will judge the people righteously.

Let the heavens rejoice and let the earth be glad:
let the sea roar, and all its creatures delight;
let the fields be joyful, and all that is in them:
then shall the trees of the wood shout for joy.
For you come to judge the earth,
with justice to make right what is wrong,
to judge the people with your truth.

All creatures of the earth will sing your praise,
for you are a God who is faithful,
for ever loyal to your covenant,
creating out of discord a harmony rare.

God of glory and splendour, whose bright radiance we see in glimpses of wonder, both rare and everyday, open our eyes and hearts, alert the nerve ends of our being, that in trembling and rapture all our fears may dissolve into joy.

THE OLD ORDER TURNED UPSIDE DOWN

*Refrain: God reigns: the gentle people inherit the earth,
the little islands rejoice to see the day.*

The foundations of your reign are rarely seen, O God,
salvation and justice are hidden away.
Clouds and darkness deepen the mystery:
faith hears but a possible cry.

The God of Justice comes:
the thunder rolls,
the lightnings flash,
the earth quakes.
Evil is burnt up by fire,
the mountains melt like wax;
the flames consume corruption,
the falling rocks hiss in the sea.

We have served vain idols,
and we are ashamed,
awed by the searing truth,
in fear and trembling brought to our knees.
Your glory lights up our faces,
and our eyes are blinded.
We have put lovers and leaders before you,
we have bowed down to our petty gods,
we have gloried in mere nothings:
like them we crumble to the dust.

The City of Peace hears its God,
and all its inhabitants rejoice.
In your judgment, O God, are the poor lifted high,
the burdens of oppression slide from their backs.
For you love those who resist evil,
you guard the life of the faithful,
you sustain them when held in the grip
of the cruel and greedy and hateful.

Your promised day dawns, O God,
a day of gladness for the true of heart.
Your reign spreads fair before us,
like a banquet prepared for a homecoming.
Those who love truth flourish in your presence,
their faces glow in the light of your welcome.
The courageous and faithful sing for joy,
and give thanks to your glorious name.

In the day of your vindication, O God, we shall laugh and sing as we never have before. From our bellies will flow the ripples of joy, the living water that makes the desert bloom and the true of heart delight in one another's love.

THE SONG OF A RENEWED CREATION

Refrain: Praise to the God who makes all things new;
let all creation sing a new song.

We praise you, O God, with a new song,
for you have done marvellous things.
With your own right hand and with your holy arm,
with the strength of weakness and the endurance of waiting,
you have achieved the greatest of victories,
bringing triumph from the midst of defeat.

So you have declared your salvation,
showing justice in the sight of the peoples.
You have remembered your mercy and faithfulness
towards the house of Israel;
your salvation has shone forth
even to the far-flung islands of the world.

Show yourselves joyful in God, all you peoples,
sing, rejoice, and give thanks.
We praise you, O God, upon the harp,
singing a psalm of thanksgiving,
with trumpets and echoing horns,
showing ourselves joyful in your presence.

Let the sea roar, and all its creatures,
the round earth, and those who dwell on it.
Let the streams clap their hands,
and let the hills be joyful before you.

For you have come to judge the earth,
justified at last in your sight,
and judging the people with justice,
with a mercy beyond our comparing,
O holy, compassionate, and most loving God.

Faithful Creator, ever striving with your creation, with nature, with your
people, with the One who embodied your will, bringing new and unexpected
life out of despair and death, work still in these our days, that we may sing
a new song to your glory.

HOLY IS GOD

Refrain: Holy, holy, holy is the living God,
holy in the awesome intimacy of love,
holy in the terrible demands of love,
holy in the silent suffering of love.

Holy God, you reign throughout the universe,
enthroned as a king majestic and just,
kneeling before us as a healer with wounds,
touching our foreheads as a woman who is wise.
Creatures of light and darkness surround you,
eyes glistening with tears of thanksgiving.

Yours is the power that holds,
the power of justice and love.
Yours is the holiness that sears,
bringing to light our falsehoods.
The prophets, the priests, and the wise,
Moses and Aaron, Samuel and Solomon,
call assured upon your name,
knowing that you will teach them,
showing them how to lead the people,
burning into them your holiness,
never yielding the commandment to love,
refusing to let any of us sink deep
into the mire and oblivion of sin.

Holy was your presence in the love of your Christ,
always in places the pious rejected,
born in a cave among a people oppressed,
suffering the hidden cost of forgiveness,
embracing the outcast who were deemed impure,
dying disgraced and disfigured,
even on a cross that was holy and hopeful.

Holy God, teach us not to be afraid of anything or anyone you have created,
however threatened or repelled we may be. Fill us with your Holy Spirit, the
holiness that draws near to transform, the Spirit that finds its home, as you
did, in our flesh and blood.

A JOYFUL PEOPLE

Refrain: We joy in your steadfast love,
we rejoice and are thankful.

Let the whole earth be joyful in you, O God,
serve you with gladness,
and celebrate your presence with a song.

For we know that you are creating us,
you have made us and we belong to you,
We are your people, and the sheep of your pasture.

We find our way into your gates with thanksgiving,
and into your house with praise.
We give you thanks and bless your holy name.

For you are gracious, your mercy is everlasting,
and your faithfulness endures from generation to generation.

Living, loving, holy God, our joy rests in you and comes from you, for we
are indeed content to be your people and we are humbled by your care for us.
You are God and there is none other. You are steadfast, faithful, loyal, and
kind. We would seek to embody your will on earth, and to trust you for all
that is to come.

ON THE EDGE OF THE CLIFF

Carter flexed his stiff fingers.

"Hold on tight, you guys," he said. "Here I come."

"We've got you!" Buzz said. All three of the others gripped the pole around the base, watching as Carter let himself off the tiny shelf where he'd been waiting.

Gripping the ledge with both hands, he lowered himself toward the top of the bamboo. One foot hooked the pole, and then both legs wrapped around it as he came low enough.

The idea was to let go of the ledge, one hand at a time, then press his palms into the cliff wall and use leverage, leg strength, and gravity to lower himself the next few crucial feet.

But the moment Carter let go with his first hand, he could tell it wasn't going to work. His other hand slipped off too soon, and he slid faster and farther than he'd intended, several feet down the pole. He'd barely taken hold of the bamboo before his own weight forced it to pull away from the wall.

"Wait!" Jane screamed, but there was nothing Carter could do. The pole came unstoppably into a vertical position, and then kept on going. The next thing he knew, it was falling toward the rocks.

"JUMP!" Buzz yelled.

The STRANDED Series

STRANDED
3
SURVIVORS

JEFF PROBST

and CHRIS TEBBETTS

PUFFIN BOOKS
An Imprint of Penguin Group (USA)

PUFFIN BOOKS
Published by the Penguin Group
Penguin Group (USA) LLC
375 Hudson Street
New York, New York 10014

USA · Canada · UK · Ireland · Australia
New Zealand · India · South Africa · China

penguin.com
A Penguin Random House Company

First published in the United States of America by Puffin Books,
an imprint of Penguin Young Readers Group, 2013

LIBRARY OF CONGRESS CATALOGING-IN-PUBLICATION DATA IS AVAILABLE

Puffin Books ISBN 978-0-14-242426-1

Printed in the United States of America

After the first *Stranded* was published in February 2013, I began to hear from lots of young readers eager to share their thoughts about *Stranded* and the characters and, most importantly, what they thought should happen next!

Some of you reached out in person and others reached me through @jeffprobst on Twitter. I loved hearing from all of you, and your ideas were very helpful.

I want to personally thank a few of you who read this third book when it was still in the manuscript stage: Sophia, Julia, Keegan, Leo, and Ireland. You are true collaborators on this book. You should take a copy to your teachers and ask for extra credit. (Sophia and Julia, your note about the jellyfish saved the day!)

I hope you all enjoy the next part of the *Stranded* adventure, and remember . . .

"The adventure you're ready for is the one you get!"

—*JP*

Several people who helped us get our story off the ground for *Stranded Book 1* were kind enough to offer some additional help along the way. Thank you (again!) to our sailing expert Jill Kuramoto; teachers Angela Galyean and Paul Lasher, along with their wonderful students at Hinesburg Community School; the man behind the big bang, Kyle Jablonski; writing and critique partners Jan Donley, Barbara Gregorich, Vicki Hayes, Ruth Horowitz, and Joe Nusbaum; and all-around muse Jonathan Radigan.

A few indispensable newbies deserve our gratitude as well. Many thanks to Dave Bernheisel from the Lightship Overfalls in Lewes, Delaware, for his nautical insights; to Dr. Ramona Salins, who detailed the hazards of wound infection for us; and to Simon Ross and Ian Tucker from the *Survivor* pyro team for a couple of truly bright ideas.

Lastly, one more enormous thank-you to our editor at Puffin, Jen Bonnell, whose voice, insight, and patience were an integral part of this storytelling adventure.

—*CT*

CHAPTER 1

Buzz Diaz looked over the edge. Straight down from where he stood, at the bottom of a hundred-foot cliff, ocean waves lapped at the rocky shoreline of Nowhere Island.

"We're going to have to climb down," Carter said.

"Tell me you're joking!" Buzz shouted. The gusting wind forced them to yell even though they were standing close together.

"I'm not joking."

"But this could kill us."

"So could staying up here," Jane chimed in.

"Yeah," Carter agreed, "just a lot more slowly."

Buzz could barely believe they were even having this conversation. The face of the wall they would have to descend was a straight drop. There were only a few places to stand and even fewer to hold on to. One slip and it was over. Nobody could survive that kind of a fall.

Ten minutes ago, they'd been *this close* to getting rescued. He, Carter, and Jane had screamed and waved like crazy as the plane passed over their little island. Buzz's own screams echoed in his head now— STOP! STOP! HELP! PLEASE!—but none of it had done them any good.

The plane was gone. So was the tree bridge they'd crossed to get up here in the first place. It had fallen straight down into the ravine on the opposite side of Lookout Point, and had nearly taken Buzz with it. He was lucky to be alive.

But Buzz wasn't feeling so lucky right now. His stomach swooped every time he looked down the cliff face, or out toward the endless Pacific Ocean that stretched away from the island. It was like looking at infinity from here.

"Are we sure this is the *better* way down?" he asked.

It wasn't a real question. They'd been back and forth across Lookout Point a dozen times. As scary as it would be scaling the ocean-facing cliffs, every other option was even worse. At least on this side, the rock was stepped in a series of plateaus and ledges, as far down as Buzz could see.

"I say we go for it," Carter announced. He nodded to Jane, the youngest of the group. "You ready?" he asked.

"I'm ready," she replied.

Easy for them to say, Buzz thought. Carter was a total jock, and Jane had already proven herself to be a natural climber here on the island.

Not Buzz. He was a natural couch potato, as much as anything else. But none of that meant anything for him anymore. The only real question now was whether he'd rather die from falling a hundred feet or from starving to death on this barren tower of rock.

"Yeah, okay," he said, barely believing the words as they came out of his own mouth. "Let's get this over with."

Carter could see how scared Jane and Buzz were. He was scared, too. Out of his mind. But so what? It didn't change what they had to do.

"I'll go first," he said, and sat himself on the edge of the cliff.

He got no argument from the other two. Carter was the strongest. That was just a fact. If a week on Nowhere Island had taught them nothing else, it was how to face up to hard, cold facts.

It seemed like forever ago that their boat had crashed onto the shore, stranding them here. The storm responsible had also separated them from Uncle Dexter and his first mate on the *Lucky Star*, Joe Kahali. Whether those two were still out there in the South Pacific somewhere was impossible to know. Carter had been the last to see them, just before the waves and high winds tore their life raft away from the *Lucky Star* and they'd disappeared into the night.

Ever since that moment, it had been up to the kids to figure everything out for themselves.

How to make fire and shelter.

How to find food and water.

How to survive.

Carter looked down the cliff face. The next nearest ledge was maybe seven feet below him—a few feet more than his own body length. He and Buzz were the same age, eleven, but Carter was taller. For Buzz, and especially Jane, who was tiny for a nine-year-old, the drop would feel even farther.

As he started to inch himself off the edge, Jane stepped forward and grabbed onto the ragged T-shirt Carter had been wearing for the last week.

"Be careful," she said.

"I'm always careful," Carter said, and grinned at his little sister. It was funny, only because they both knew it wasn't true. Nowhere Island was not a place where you could survive by being careful. You had to take some chances.

Before he could lose his nerve, Carter turned around and eased himself the rest of the way over the lip of the cliff. Pulse racing, and wind whipping in his ears, he lowered his body until he was hanging with arms fully extended. The outcropping he wanted to reach was still a foot or more down. It wasn't far, but if he missed, it was going to be a long drop to the bottom.

This was the moment of truth. He checked the distance to the ledge under his feet one more time. Took a breath. And let go.

Gravity took care of the rest. His palms scraped over the cliff wall, and the gash on his right hand from the day before lit up with a hot flash of pain. Still, it was nothing compared to the rush of the quick drop. With a jolt, he landed on the narrow piece of rock. His whole body shuddered as he found his balance, and he pressed himself into the wall as close as he could get.

Carter didn't even try to catch his breath. That would have to come later. A quick glance down past his heels showed him the vertical maze of ledges and handholds that still waited between this spot and the ground.

Seven feet down. Ninety-something to go.

Jane followed Carter's example. She turned around

on the rim of the cliff and lowered herself toward the first ledge.

"You can do it, Jane," Buzz said.

Hanging with her face toward the rock, it was a blind descent. When she let go, everything blurred, but Carter was right there as she landed. He put a firm hand on her arm and held tight.

"I've got you," he said. "That wasn't so bad, right?"

Jane only nodded. It was hard to speak with her heart running so fast. It felt as if the wind could scoop in and pull her right off the ledge without warning. Carter was trying to be encouraging, but her brother's wide eyes said otherwise. This was going to be anything *but* easy.

As Buzz started down, Jane and Carter pushed together to make room for him. Buzz moved more cautiously and not nearly as gracefully, but when his feet finally touched down next to them, he let out a huge sigh of relief.

"Okay," he muttered, maybe just to convince himself. "Okay, okay . . . let's keep going."

Level by level, they made their way down the wall,

descending like a human inchworm. Carter would advance first, then Jane, then Buzz, before Carter moved on again. Twice, they had to shuffle sideways along a ledge before they could make the next drop. Their progress was slow but steady.

And then it came to a stop. Carter had just reached a shallow ridge below Jane and Buzz when he held up a hand.

"Don't come down yet," he said.

"Why?" Buzz asked. "What is it?"

They were well past the halfway point. It looked to Jane as if the rocks of the shoreline were no more than thirty feet farther down. But the only thing she could see between where Carter stood and the ground itself was sheer cliff wall. No ledges. No handholds. Nothing.

"Carter? Are we stuck?" Jane asked, trying to stay calm.

"I don't know," Carter said. He craned his neck, looking down, left, and right. "We might be."

"Might be?" Buzz called out, the tension rising in his voice.

Carter didn't respond, but the answer was obvious to Jane. They'd just reached a dead end—fingers clinging to the cliff wall, feet balanced on narrow pieces of rock, and too high up to even think about jumping.

They weren't going anywhere.

CHAPTER 2

Vanessa picked her way along the shoreline, headed for camp as fast as she could go. It was rough, slow hiking over the black sandpapery boulders that rimmed this part of the island. More than once, she slipped and scraped her hands. The tide was coming in, too, and the breaking waves sprayed her with salt water that stung her eyes.

There was good reason to be careful. Any cut or scrape could get infected, and then good luck dealing with that. There was no first-aid kit on the island. No adults. No hospital for a thousand miles. Just *not* getting hurt was like an added responsibility.

Still, it was hard not to rush. There was so much she had to tell the others!

She'd run away from camp before dawn, feeling as if she'd never be able to face Carter, Jane, and Buzz again. Not after what had happened the night before. As the oldest, she was supposed to be looking out for her younger siblings. Instead, she'd fallen asleep on her own watch. Jane's precious journal had dropped into the fire, and then—even worse—the flames had spread to their little bamboo shelter on the beach. Within minutes, the whole thing had burned to the ground.

But all of that was secondary now, compared to what had happened since. Traveling up the shore that morning, Vanessa had stumbled upon a cove none of them knew about. There was a freshwater stream, and an old shipwreck tucked into the inlet. The water alone was like gold in a place like this—plus who knew what other kind of supplies might be waiting for them on that ship?

It was a question she would have answered for herself, if not for the other discovery she'd made. In a clearing overlooking the cove, Vanessa had also found something like a small graveyard. A wooden cross was stuck into the ground there, and a single human skeleton lay in the underbrush.

The remains had most definitely been human. There was no mistaking the shape of the skull she'd seen, or the long arm and leg bones. Vanessa shuddered just thinking about it. Whoever had crashed on the island before them had also died here.

Whether or not she'd mention the graveyard, she wasn't sure yet. It was probably better to focus on the positive news first, she thought. It wouldn't do any good to—

"VANESSA!"

A shout came from somewhere nearby. Right away, Vanessa recognized Buzz's voice, but she couldn't tell where it was coming from. Straight ahead, she could see their familiar beach, where the rocky part of the shoreline gave way to soft sand. She could even see their camp and the burned remains of their shelter. But no Buzz, or anyone else.

"Buzz?" she called out.

"Up here!" he said. "Help!"

Vanessa's gaze traveled up the rock wall on her right—and there, maybe thirty feet off the ground, were Buzz, Jane, and Carter.

Her voice came out in a scream. "What are you doing? How did you get up there?"

"We didn't," Jane said. "We got down."

"*What?*"

"Just help us!" Carter yelled.

Even from this distance, the fear on their faces was clear. Buzz and Jane both stood balanced on a tiny outcropping that was barely wider than their feet. Carter sat just below them, on his own lip of rock.

Vanessa stepped from black boulder to black boulder, hurrying closer. "Do we still have any rope?" she called up. She hadn't taken any stock of their supplies since the fire.

"Yeah," Carter said, "but that doesn't do us any good. We don't have any way to anchor it up here."

"Can you see some other way for us to climb down?" Buzz called.

Vanessa scanned the cliff face for any kind of

handholds they might reach. "I don't see anything," she said. Behind her, the ocean was at least fifty feet away. It was too far to jump, in any case. The beach was off to the side, and much closer, but landing in sand wasn't like landing in water. Any of them could easily break a bone—or worse, if they hit the rocks.

"There has to be something," Jane said. "Think!"

Vanessa's mind raced. She squinted over at their beach camp, looking for anything they might use. Mostly, she just saw the burned-out shelter. Several charred pieces of bamboo lay in the sand.

"Anything?" Buzz called down. "There must be a way—"

"Bamboo!" Vanessa shouted as it came to her.

"What?" Jane shouted.

There was no time to waste. "I'll be right back!" Vanessa said, already rushing off the rocks, down to the sand, and into camp.

The axe was right there, next to the dead fire pit. She snatched it up and kept moving. The bamboo grew in a grove just a few minutes up the beach, but she'd still have to find a long enough piece. Even then, could this actually work? Would she be able to get the others off that cliff wall? Or would it end in disaster?

The answer to all of it was—maybe. But now was not the time for questions.

Watching Vanessa run off, Jane wiggled her toes. After standing on the tiny ledge for so long, her foot was starting to fall asleep. The sun beat down on them, and her hands were sweaty where she tried to grip the rock wall behind her.

She couldn't stop thinking about the plane, either. It had flown right over the island, close enough to show the blue markings on its wings and tail. It was like torture, thinking about where they might have been by now if the plane had spotted them. Wrapped up in a blanket with something to eat? On their way back to civilization? On their way home?

"Jane, you okay?" Carter asked from his spot just below her on the wall.

"I will be," she told him, even though it felt like

a lie. It was always harder when she thought about home. But complaining wasn't going to help anyone.

Finally, Vanessa reappeared on the beach. Jane could see her dragging a long green cane of freshly cut bamboo behind her.

"I'm coming!" she shouted. "Just hold on!"

All Jane, Buzz, or Carter could do was watch as Vanessa worked her way back to the rocks of Dead Man's Shelf. That was Jane's name for it—this piece of shoreline where their sailboat had crashed into the island.

When Vanessa got there, she hauled the long pole up onto the rocks and struggled to get it into place. Bit by bit, she managed to pivot the bamboo until one end was directly beneath the spot where Jane waited with her brothers. Vanessa positioned herself at the opposite end of the pole and lifted it up, walking it hand over hand into an upright position.

It was awkward going. Twice, Vanessa lost her grip and had to start over. But on the third try, the bamboo slowly went vertical, and then just past, until it was leaning against the cliff face.

Jane's heart sunk. The bamboo was *almost* tall enough, but not quite. The top of the pole had come to rest a few feet below the ledge where Carter was perched.

"Can you get to it?" Vanessa called up.

"I don't think so!" Jane said.

"Yes," Carter answered over her, his voice set with determination. Already, he was lying flat on his piece of ledge. With one arm extended, he was just able to wrap a hand around the top of the bamboo cane.

"See? We can do this," Carter said. "Come on, Jane. You first."

Jane wasn't so sure, but she edged herself off the rock where she'd been standing with Buzz for the last hour or more. She eased down into the tiny space next to Carter and stood between his legs.

"I can hold the pole steady from up here while you slide down," Carter said. "Then Buzz can go next."

"But then what are you going to do?" Jane asked, alarmed all over again. It wasn't a hundred-foot drop anymore, but it was still enough to kill any of them if they fell.

"We'll figure that out later," Carter said.

"But what if—"

"What if what, Jane?" her brother snapped. "Some-one has to go last."

He was right, Jane knew. There was no good answer here, and nothing left to talk about. Heart thudding, she squeezed down to a sitting position next to Carter. He kept one hand on the bamboo. With the other, he hooked Jane under her arm and helped ease her off the ledge until she could reach the pole.

First, Jane's legs wrapped around it. Then as she came low enough, she grabbed on with both hands.

"Have you got it?" Carter asked.

"I . . . guess," Jane said. For some reason, the bamboo had looked thicker and sturdier from above. The whole thing bowed under her weight, bringing her even closer to the cliff wall. But there was no going back now. With a deep breath, she let go just enough to slide down a few feet, and then stopped again.

"Good job, Janie!" Vanessa called out. "Keep going!"

Jane loosened her grip again and dropped a bit farther.

Then again, and again.

The bamboo burned against her skin as she went. It wasn't a smooth ride, but the ground came up quickly. Soon, she was standing safely on the rocks next to Vanessa.

There was no time for talking. The girls quickly positioned themselves on either side of the pole as Buzz got ready to work his way down.

His descent was slower than Jane's had been. His body scraped against the cliff face as he squeaked his way along, foot by foot. By the time he touched down and let go of the bamboo, his arms and legs were marred with painful-looking, deep-red burn marks. Still, he looked more relieved than anything.

Now came the really tricky part. It was Carter's turn.

Carter flexed his stiff fingers. His hands were raw from gripping rock, and the gash on his palm had opened up. This wasn't going to be easy.

"Hold on tight, you guys," he said. "Here I come."

"We've got you!" Buzz said. All three of the others gripped the pole around the base, watching as Carter let himself off the tiny shelf where he'd been waiting.

Gripping the ledge with both hands, he lowered himself toward the top of the bamboo. One foot hooked the pole, and then both legs wrapped around it as he came low enough.

The idea was to let go of the ledge, one hand at a time, then press his palms into the cliff wall and use leverage, leg strength, and gravity to lower himself the next few crucial feet.

But the moment Carter let go with his first hand, he could tell it wasn't going to work. His other hand slipped off too soon, and he slid faster and farther than he'd intended, several feet down the pole. He'd barely taken hold of the bamboo before his own weight forced it to pull away from the wall.

"Wait!" Jane screamed, but there was nothing Carter could do. The pole came unstoppably into a vertical position, and then kept on going. The next thing he knew, it was falling toward the rocks.

"JUMP!" Buzz yelled.

He saw Buzz throw himself against the pole and felt a hard jerk from below. The bamboo's direction shifted. It was falling toward the beach now. In the fraction of a second Carter had left, he realized what Buzz meant for him to do. He thrust as hard as he could, pushing himself away from the falling pole. His eyes took in a blur of rock, sea, and sky—just before he landed in the sand. A shock of pain came up through his legs. He absorbed what he could and rolled several times before coming to a stop.

He was on his back. His eyes were squeezed shut, and he tried to figure out if anything was broken.

"Carter!" Jane's voice came from nearby. The others were there now, kneeling next to him. Someone's hand was on his arm.

"Can you sit up?" Vanessa said.

Carter blinked several times and squinted into the hot sun. He wiggled his toes. Bent his knees.

"I think so," he said.

As they got him onto his feet, it was a relief to find that he could walk on his own. The only real pain came from the throbbing cut on his hand. But that didn't seem like much, compared to what could have happened.

The point was, he'd made it down in one piece.

They all had. And they'd done it together.

CHAPTER 3

Back at camp, everyone flopped out in the shade. It had been a long morning. Vanessa could hardly wait to tell the others about the cove she'd found, but they had a story of their own to tell first.

Jane explained that a plane had flown by that morning. Vanessa had never even heard it from where she'd been.

It was the first and only plane any of them had seen since they'd been stranded here a week ago. Despite Carter, Jane, and Buzz's best efforts, everything had gone horribly wrong. The tree bridge they'd been using to reach Lookout Point was gone now, and they'd never gotten a real chance to signal the plane.

Tears showed in Buzz's eyes as he told his part of the story.

"I'm really sorry, you guys," he said. "If I hadn't fallen off the tree bridge, we could have gotten up there in time. We might have been on our way home by now—"

He stopped and bit his lip. That word—*home*— seemed to weigh heavily on all of them.

"You didn't fall, Buzz," Carter said. "The tree fell. And that was *my* fault."

Vanessa stared at each of the boys in turn. It was the closest thing to an apology she'd ever heard from Carter. Usually, he was too stubborn for anything like that. But then again, Carter had changed out here. They all had. And it seemed like the perfect time for some good news.

"Listen, you guys," she said. "First of all, it was stupid of me to run off like that. I'm really sorry, and I promise it won't happen again. But you're not going to believe what else happened. I found this cove up the shore. There's an old wrecked boat, and—"

Carter raised his head from where he lay in the sand. "What kind of boat?" he asked. Jane and Buzz sat up, too.

"I don't know," Vanessa said. "Not a sailboat. Some kind of ship. I didn't go on board."

"Why not?" Carter asked.

Vanessa paused. The real answer was because she'd found the grave and skeletal remains before she could explore the ship. But the whole point was to focus on positive news right now.

"Because I found a freshwater stream," she said. "And we don't have to go through those nasty caves to get to it, like the last one."

At that, all three of the others jumped up. The only fresh water they'd found until now was on the other side of a pitch-black maze of caves. Without any flashlight or torch to lead the way, it might as well have been on another island.

"Are you serious? Why didn't you say so?" Buzz asked.

"Let's go," Carter said. "Right now. I want to see this ship."

"I want a drink," Jane said.

"I want about eighteen drinks," Buzz said.

Vanessa stood and looked up the shore. It wasn't far to the cove, but it was tough going over that long stretch of volcanic rock. The others were already exhausted from their climb down.

Still, that didn't seem to matter, compared with the prospect of fresh water and supplies.

"All right, let's go," she said. "But just so you know, it's not going to be easy getting there."

Buzz had never explored the island's shore in this direction. None of them had, except for Vanessa. She was right about the slow going over the rocks, too. It took the better part of an hour to reach the cove.

But finally, he stood at the mouth of the wide inlet, staring at the big ship Vanessa had told them about.

It was strange, seeing anything man-made here. Anything from the outside world. The ship was maybe twice the length of the *Lucky Star*. That would make it a hundred feet long. The whole thing was grounded along its starboard side, at the far end of the cove.

"Where's the drinking water?" Carter asked.

Vanessa pointed past the bow of the ship. Behind it, water was seeping down a low, curved rock wall that formed the U-shape of the inlet itself. The stone was dark with moisture, and it was covered in the green moss and algae that seemed to grow everywhere in this quiet, shady spot.

All four of them—Jane, Carter, Buzz, and Vanessa—took off running. They splashed through shallow water, following the curve of the cove until they came to the stream at the back. It trickled down in several places. To get a drink Buzz pressed his face sideways against the mossy rock and let the cold water run into his mouth. It felt like suddenly waking up. Like a cool shower for his throat and insides.

For several long silent moments, nobody spoke. Carter and Jane had picked their own spots, where they gulped the water down in fast, loud sips. Vanessa stood back and waited for them to finish before she took her own drink.

Once he'd had his fill, Buzz turned his attention back to the boat. Its starboard hull loomed over the back of the cove like a giant metal wall. It looked as though it had been painted blue once, but most of it had gone to rust. A few black holes showed where the metal had corroded all the way through.

Five minutes ago, the idea of climbing up and exploring the ship had seemed overwhelming to Buzz. Now he was excited to see what they might find.

"Can we live here?" Jane asked.

"Why not?" Carter said. "It's huge. And the water supply's right here. We can't keep hiking back and forth over those rocks every time we need a drink."

Buzz liked the idea already. The boat would be dry, and there were probably real bunks on board. It also meant not having to rebuild their burned-out shelter. Trying to sleep on bamboo the last several nights had been like torture, anyway.

"Maybe we should look inside first," Jane said.

"Let's do it," Carter said, and started toward the ship.

"Actually," Vanessa said. "Hold on a second. There's something else you guys should see first."

Buzz looked at his sister. She had a strange expression on her face, but he couldn't tell what it was about.

"What kind of something else?" Carter asked.

Vanessa pointed over her shoulder, to a clearing in the woods. It sat at the top of the rock wall with the stream, and overlooked the whole cove. As for what might be up there, Buzz could only wonder.

But Vanessa seemed intent on showing them. Already, she was climbing up that way.

"Vanessa? What's going on?" he asked.

"Just come on," she said without looking back. "It's better if I show you."

Carter climbed up to the clearing behind Vanessa, Buzz, and Jane. It didn't take much effort, but by the time he reached it, all three of the others had stopped.

In fact, they'd gone perfectly still. And then Carter saw why.

Right there, stuck into the ground, was a handmade wooden cross. The wood was rough with age, just two cracked gray planks nailed together. There was no name, or markings of any kind.

"Is that a . . . grave?" he asked.

"I think so," Vanessa said. "And there's more. Don't freak out, but there's a bunch of bones over there—"

"What?" Buzz asked.

"Actually, not just bones," Vanessa said. "More like a skeleton."

Carter felt a chill run through him. He looked in the direction Vanessa had pointed, but he couldn't see anything.

She led them across the clearing and pulled back some low-hanging vines. What Carter saw there on the ground looked like some kind of movie prop, even though it clearly wasn't. He'd seen skeletons before, at the Museum of Science and Industry back home in Chicago.

This one was definitely real. It was half sunk into

the ground and mostly the color of dirt from however many years it had been here.

Jane reached over and took Carter's hand.

"Do you think there are more?" Buzz asked. "That's a big boat for two people."

"It's possible the others got rescued," Vanessa said.

"Or maybe there's more than one person buried under that cross," Carter said. He looked down at the skeleton again and shivered. "This guy was probably the last one."

"That's what I was thinking," Vanessa said. "There wasn't anyone left to . . . take care of him."

Only Jane stayed silent. She pulled her hand out of Carter's and knelt down by the remains. Slowly, she reached out and laid her fingers over the delicate hand bones of whoever this person had been.

"Don't touch it!" Vanessa said.

"Why not?" Jane asked. She kept her gaze down, and Carter could see the tears on her cheeks.

"Jane?" he asked.

"We were so close to being rescued," she said in a

faraway voice. "That plane . . . it was right there. And now . . ."

She didn't finish, but Carter knew what she was thinking. If these adults with their big ship had never gotten off the island, what did that mean for the four of them?

Carter's thoughts churned while the jungle hummed with the sound of a million bugs and birds all around them. Finally, he spoke up again.

"We need to get real about this," he said.

"What do you mean?" Vanessa asked him. "About what?"

He looked out toward the mouth of the cove, and beyond that, the bluest ocean any of them had ever seen. "That plane might have been our only chance," Carter said. "If they were looking for us, then they just crossed this place off their list—"

"You don't know that," Vanessa countered. "Besides, it's not the only plane out there. Beth and Dad are doing everything they can. You know they are."

"Hold on, Vanessa," Buzz said. "Carter's right. I mean, we should definitely build a new signal fire and make sure we're ready if another plane comes. But we need to think about what happens if . . ."

"If what, Buzz?" Vanessa asked stubbornly.

"If it never comes."

Buzz was crying now, too. They all were. Carter could feel the tears stinging at the corners of his eyes. A week ago, he might have tried to hide them, but it didn't seem worth it anymore.

"Why are you guys being like this?" Vanessa asked.

"We're not being like anything," Carter said. "It's just facts. There's nothing anyone can do for this guy, but we do need a place to live. And we can sure use his ship."

"Actually," Jane spoke up in a small voice, "there *is* something we can do for him."

Carter stopped and looked at her. Usually when Jane spoke up, it was for a good reason. "Like what?" he asked.

"We can give him a funeral," Jane answered. "The one he never had."

An hour later, Buzz stood back and looked at what they'd accomplished. It had been tough work—he was covered with sweat—but he was glad they'd listened to Jane.

The ground here was too rocky for digging, even if they'd had a shovel. Instead, they'd gathered all the big stones they could find and formed a mound over the skeletal remains. Jane said the mound was called a *cairn*, though she couldn't remember where the word came from. After the last of the rocks had been stacked, she'd picked several white and yellow flowers from the woods and placed them on top.

Now everyone stood around, shifting on tired feet. "Should we say something?" Buzz asked. It seemed like the right thing to do, but he wasn't sure what to say.

Then quietly, Jane started in.

"You died here alone, and nobody ever knew it," she said. She was facing the cairn and clearly speaking to whoever was inside. "Now we know it, and if we ever get out of here, other people will know it, too. Nobody's going to forget about you. That's a promise."

"Also, thank you for the ship," Vanessa said.

It was a strange thing to say, Buzz thought, but it also seemed right. He hadn't thought of anything to offer himself, although several questions had been running through his mind for the last hour.

What happened here? Why were these people never rescued? What had they done wrong?

Maybe the answer was . . . nothing. Maybe they'd done everything they could. But if they *had* made a mistake, Buzz thought, and if he and the others could figure out what it was, then maybe—just maybe— it could bring them a step closer to getting rescued themselves.

And if that happened, then maybe these people would have died for something. To help save the four of them.

Buzz realized *that* might be a nice thing to say, once he'd thought it. But the moment had passed. Carter, Jane, and Vanessa were already turning away, headed down to the ship.

It was time to get back to work.

CHAPTER 4

Carter reached up with his good hand and pulled himself onto the deck of the abandoned ship. With the funeral behind them, his thoughts had turned back to whatever might be waiting for them on board.

Vanessa, Buzz, and Jane scrambled up behind him, and they worked their way toward the ship's two-level wheelhouse. It sat like a small building on the main deck, with doors on either side, port and starboard.

When Carter reached the port entrance, he saw at a glance how dead the place was inside. An instrument panel near the door was smashed and dented, its old glass gauges covered in a thick layer of grime. Vines grew in through the spaces where the windows used to be and ran in a tangle all around the room.

"I think this is communications over here," Vanessa said. The first thing on everyone's mind was the radio—but it didn't take long to rule out that possibility. Vanessa flipped several switches and turned a few levers, but nothing happened. It was all just junk by now.

Carter went straight up a set of steep metal stairs to find the captain's wheel on the top level. A dead clock above the broken-out windows had stopped at 10:35. There seemed to be some navigation equipment as well, but it was just as lifeless as everything else. He didn't see any paper charts, either.

"There's more stairs over here," Buzz's voice came from below, followed by a metal groan and echoing footsteps.

Then Carter heard Vanessa call out. "Buzz, slow down," she said. "Wait for me."

"Well, come on, then," Buzz answered back. "I think there might be—"

Whatever he said next was swallowed up by

another metallic groan, a loud snapping sound, and then an enormous crash.

Carter raced back down to the main level of the wheelhouse. Jane stood alone in an open hatchway at the back, looking into the space below. If any stairs had been there a minute ago, they were gone now. All Carter could see was the hole left behind and a cloud of gray dust.

"Buzz?" he shouted. "Vanessa?"

Vanessa struggled to catch her breath. The fall had knocked the wind right out of her. Buzz started coughing first. As the cloud of dust and particles cleared, she could see him on the floor, rubbing his head.

Her own first breath turned into a cough as well. She covered her mouth and hacked up a lungful of dust while Jane and Carter scrambled down to reach them. The ceilings were low here. It wasn't a far drop from the main deck to this one.

"Is everyone okay?" Carter asked.

"I think so," Vanessa said. She was getting used to being banged up in a way that she never would have shrugged off at home. They all were.

As the dust continued to clear, the space around them revealed itself. They were in a small plain room, with portholes on either side. There were two long tables with matching benches, and a line of framed maps on the wall, mostly with broken glass. A stack of wooden pallets sat in the corner. Vanessa recognized the gray, cracked planks right away. They matched the wood of the grave marker up in the clearing.

"We can use those for firewood," Carter said.

"And we can push one of these tables over," Vanessa said. "That'll make getting back out of here easier."

Working together, she and Carter dragged the collapsed staircase off to the side and pushed the nearest table into place, under the hatch door above.

From where they stood, narrow passages extended away in both directions. Toward the stern, Vanessa could see several open cabin doors.

"Here's the galley!" Jane called out from the other

direction. Immediately, Vanessa turned and followed the boys back that way to see.

It didn't take long to ransack the tiny kitchen and come up empty-handed. There were some pots and pans, and dozens of utensils, but that was it. Anything resembling a food locker was disappointingly empty. Whoever had been shipwrecked here before them had obviously gone through everything there was to eat. *Before they died,* Vanessa thought. It was depressing, but there was no use dwelling on it.

"Let's keep moving," she said, and peered down the corridor in the opposite direction. "What do you think's over there?"

Jane followed the others into the corridor that led toward the stern of the boat. There were two cabin doors on each side, all of them open.

"Everyone take a cabin," Carter said.

Jane turned and stepped over the raised sill of the doorway on her left. The tiny room looked more like an office than sleeping quarters. Besides a single porthole, the walls were covered with wire mesh shelving. A mess of old rotted cardboard boxes sat on some of the shelves. Others were piled in the corners. A quick look showed her they were all too stained and mildewed to be of any interest.

Jane turned her attention to the metal desk bolted against the wall. On the desktop, several old books sat in a stack, but the titles on their spines were written in an alphabet she didn't recognize. There was also a clear plastic paperweight with a sand dollar inside, and several empty metal cups. In one of the cups, she found a broken-off pencil, and immediately stuck it in her pocket.

On the wall over the desk was another framed map. Looking more closely, she saw that it was crisscrossed with longitude and latitude markings, and that several cities on the map were marked in English: Busan, Pyongyang, Seoul. It was the last one that Jane recognized.

"I think this ship is from Korea!" she called out to the others. She could see Carter across the hall, rooting through one of the sleeping cabins.

"Check it out!" he said. He held up a metal spool of some kind. "I think this is fishing line. And if we can find some wire, we can make hooks!"

It was a thrill, starting to unearth some of the ship's left-behind treasures. And its secrets, too.

Jane started opening desk drawers next, and she quickly found the one thing she'd most been hoping for. In the bottom left drawer, a stack of four leather-bound journals sat waiting for her. As she took them out and thumbed the yellowing pages, she saw more unfamiliar handwriting—Korean language, she supposed.

Best of all, each book had at least a few blank pages at the back. She could use those to restart her own journal, after losing the last one in the fire. It was tempting to sit down and start writing right away.

For the first several days on Nowhere Island, she'd recorded everything on video. It had begun as a report for her fifth-grade class. But after the shipwreck, it became more like a diary of life on the island.

When the camera's batteries ran down, she'd switched to writing by hand, in Uncle Dexter's captain's journal from the *Lucky Star*. Somewhere along the way, the journal became something else again—a way of not going crazy, maybe, or just a way to capture it all and hold it in one place.

Whatever it was, Jane hugged the journals to her chest, feeling happy for the first time in days. After a truly horrible morning, the afternoon was turning out to be much, much better.

Fresh water, a dry place to sleep, and a new journal. It wasn't a lot, but it sure felt that way.

"Hey, you guys!" Buzz shouted from his cabin down the hall. "Come look at this!"

He stood in one of the three sleeping chambers, staring at the floor. A manhole cover of some kind was sunk into the roughly textured metal deck. He'd seen several throughout the ship already, each one of them tightly bolted down.

Until this one.

Whoever had been here before had left it open for

some reason. Half a dozen loose bolts and an old rusted wrench lay on the floor nearby. Two more bolts were half screwed into their holes, holding the cover in place.

Vanessa appeared in the door. "What is it?" she asked. Carter was there now, too, and Jane squeezed between both of them to see.

"I don't know," Buzz said. "I was just going to find out."

He picked up the wrench and fitted it to the first bolt. It was stiff and took some effort, but soon it loosened right up. He was able to finish taking it out with just his fingers.

The same was true on the second one.

With the bolts removed, there was still the matter of prying the big steel disc out of its place in the floor. Carter, Vanessa, and Jane gathered around, and they all crammed their fingers into the small space the bolts had left behind.

"Ready?" Carter said. "One, two, three—"

Buzz heaved along with the others. The cover was snugly fitted. It seemed to have formed a seal over the hole, or whatever was down there. It took several tries before it came up even a fraction of an inch.

"Again!" Buzz said. "It's coming!"

They all lifted again. With a scrape of metal and the sound of sucking air, the cover finally came free. They shuffled it to the side, then let it drop onto the deck with a huge clang.

The next thing Buzz noticed was the smell. A harsh chemical odor poured up and out of the dark space beneath the floor.

Jane gagged. "What is that?" she asked.

"Oh, man!" Carter said, backing up. "Did we just open a sewer?"

"I don't think so," Buzz said. He lifted the collar of his T-shirt over his mouth and nose before he looked down inside.

Just below floor level, he could see the top of a ladder built into the side of whatever tank they'd just opened. An old stained rope was tied to the top rung and extended down into the darkness. For about the hundredth time in the last week, Buzz wished for a flashlight.

Instead, he reached down and grabbed hold of the

rope. It was greasy and also sticky in his hands as he started to pull.

"Buzz? What are you doing?" Vanessa asked.

There was some resistance on the line at first. Then it gave way all at once. A bucket appeared out of the black, hanging on the end of the rope. He could see it was filled with a thick, dark liquid of some kind.

Buzz's pulse quickened, thinking about what this might be. The others all stepped back while he lifted the full bucket up and out of the hole.

"What is it?" Jane asked.

"I think it's fuel," Buzz replied.

"Fuel?" Carter asked. "Like, gas?"

Buzz shrugged. He didn't know what these boats ran on. All he knew was that they'd just found something that *might* make life around camp easier. Which, in a place like this, was like striking gold.

Or maybe more like oil.

CHAPTER 5

For the rest of the afternoon, everyone kept busy, exploring their new home and bringing any useful items up onto the main deck. Jane catalogued it all in her journal, and everyone set to making what they could out of what they'd found.

Now, as the sun dipped to the west, Vanessa stood on the rocks at the mouth of the cove, dangling her homemade fishing pole in the water.

The pole wasn't much—a willowy branch from the woods, a piece of the plastic line Carter had found, and a wire she'd sharpened against the rocks to make a hook. With a snail for bait, she felt ready to catch some dinner.

Or more like desperate for it.

Up to now, Jane had proven herself to be the brain of the group. Buzz was the one who knew the most about survival, and Carter was the muscle. All Vanessa knew about herself anymore was that she was the oldest. It didn't seem to be adding up to much lately.

Nobody had said whether or not they wanted her to be the group leader anymore. Not since she'd run off that morning, before everything had gone so wrong.

And maybe that was for the best, Vanessa thought. Maybe they didn't need a leader anymore. What they needed right now was fish.

Back at the ship, she could see Buzz, busily working on the campfire. He'd brought up several bucketloads of sand to make a big fire pit right there on the ship's steel deck, surrounded by a ring of flat stones from the beach. It hadn't taken him long after that to find a broken glass bottle he could use to refract the sunlight and get a flame started, like he'd done before. Already, he had a good blaze going near the ship's bow.

Meanwhile, Carter was up in the woods, crashing around and scavenging for anything they could use, or eat. And Jane sat on a rock near the water's edge, scribbling away in her new journal.

"Any nibbles yet?" Jane asked, for what felt like the hundredth time.

"Not yet," Vanessa said. She was trying to be patient. It had been at least two hours, and she hadn't even gotten the tiniest pull on her line.

It was frustrating. They'd all been swimming in this water and seen a million fish just under the surface. But that was farther out, where the coral reef seemed to attract endless numbers of them.

The reef was where they needed to go, she thought. Somehow, they'd have to get themselves out onto the water. There was plenty of bamboo around. Maybe she could figure out how to make a workable raft.

But not today. The sun was already on its way down. It would be getting dark soon.

"I'm going in," she said to Jane. "Do you want to come back with me?"

Jane closed her journal, using her finger as a bookmark as Vanessa came near. "Not yet," she said. "I'm going to write a little more."

Vanessa looked to the horizon, where the sky had just started to dim. She could hear the bugs, warming up for their all-night chorus in the jungle. She could even smell the cool night air coming on.

It was all strangely familiar now, as if her senses had gotten sharper out here. She could spot the hermit crabs in the sand even when they weren't moving, and she swore she could tell the different calls of the cicada, the loudest insect she'd ever heard. Or maybe she was just imagining it.

She looked down at Jane again. "Don't . . ." she started to say, but then changed her mind and headed toward the ship.

"Don't what?" Jane asked after her.

"Nothing," Vanessa said. It was tempting to tell her not to stay out here too long. The mosquitoes always got worse around sunset, and it was important for the four of them to stick together after dark.

But Jane knew that. Even more, Jane could make

her own decisions around here. She'd proven that by now.

They all had.

Jane sat quietly, waiting until Vanessa had gone back to the ship. Then she opened her new journal and silently read what she'd written so far.

Dear Mom and Dad,

First of all, I'm not going to call you Mom and Eric anymore. Just Mom and Dad, if that's okay with you. I miss you both so much! I wish like anything you were here.

Wait. No, I don't. I wish WE were THERE . . .wherever you are. When I think about it, I like to imagine you on a plane, somewhere just out of sight. Like you're almost here to pick us up and take us home.

I probably shouldn't even think about that. It hurts when I do. But I also can't help it. I know you're out there—SOME-WHERE. And I know you're looking for us.

You'd probably want to know that we're taking care of each other. Vanessa's a really good older sister. I'm glad she's here with me. Buzz and Carter, too. I wish you could know that, because I'm sure you're worrying about us. You're probably even wondering if we're still alive.

Well, we are.

And we all love you.

And we MISS YOU. Huge, like the ocean.

xoxoxoxo, Jane (and Vanessa and Carter and Buzz)

P.S. If anyone finds this note, PLEASE send it to Elizabeth Benson and Eric Diaz at the address on the bottom of

this page. It's more important than you
can ever know. Thank you!

Jane carefully tore the page out of her journal.
With another quick look back, she made sure she
was still alone. Then she reached down between the
rocks and pulled up the old bottle she'd found in a
corner of the ship's galley. It smelled terrible on the
inside but still had a screw cap to keep the whole
thing watertight.

Standing with her back to the ship, she quickly
rolled the letter into a tight scroll, slid it into the
bottle, and sealed the whole thing up again.

It was stupid to throw a bottled note into the ocean.
It was babyish, and impossible to think that the note
might actually reach someone out there. If Carter,
Buzz, or Vanessa knew she was doing it, they'd
probably laugh her right off the island.

But none of that mattered. Above all, she kept
thinking about something her mother liked to say. *If
you don't try, you'll never know.*

It couldn't hurt, anyway. Even just writing the

letter felt good, like making a tiny connection to the real world back home.

Looking toward the horizon, Jane held the bottle in both hands. She gave it a quick kiss for good luck and threw it as far as she could. It splashed into the ocean, several yards offshore, and bobbed there, not going anywhere for the time being.

Jane watched for a few seconds more, then turned away and headed back to the ship. She'd done what she could. The rest was up to luck.

Carter stood perfectly still. *Don't move, Benson,* he told himself. *Not even so much as a twitch.*

It was dim in the woods. The sun had started to go down, and everything was washed in the pale blue color of dusk. But one thing stood out. It was the tan-and-black-banded snake, slithering off the tree in front of him.

It moved slowly off a low branch, taking its time. Carter wondered if the snake was aware of him or not. If so, it didn't seem to care. The thing had never seen a human before—that was for sure. It was just going about its business, heading for the carpet of leaves and brush on the forest floor.

Carter's heart raced with adrenaline, but there was no fear. He was too hungry for that. He'd heard of people eating rattlers before. Why not this one, too? It was at least three feet long, and thick. Which meant *meaty*, Carter thought. Its tiny black eyes were barely visible on either side of its flat, triangular head.

That was what he'd aim for—the head. But first, he needed a weapon.

Keeping his feet planted, he looked around for anything he could easily grab. A gray fist-sized rock sat in the weeds just a few feet away. It was smaller than he would have liked, but it would have to do. Moving slowly, he crouched down and picked up the rock with his good hand, never taking his eyes off the snake.

Now, he waited. The snake paused and advanced, paused and advanced, working its way toward the base of the tree trunk. Eventually, it slid onto flat ground, where it stopped again.

This was his chance. Any doubts he might have had were drowned out by the sharp, empty ache in his stomach. In one fluid motion, Carter dropped and brought the rock down on the snake's head with all the strength he had.

It was a direct hit. But the snake reacted with a speed of its own. Its tail and back half kicked up, coiling around Carter's leg. He felt a squeeze on his thigh as he jumped back. His fingers wrapped around the snake's leathery body, and he whipped it off his leg, dropping it to the ground again. Without pause, he stepped forward and pinned the thing with his sneaker.

For a full minute or more, the snake's body continued to move. It writhed under his foot, slowly curling and uncurling, until finally, it went still.

Carter looked down at his kill. He prodded it with his toe to make sure it was dead. Then he picked it up and turned to go.

It was only as he headed back to the ship that his

nerves started to kick in. His hand trembled as he walked, with the lifeless snake hanging in his grip. He realized he'd barely breathed the whole time, and his lungs worked to catch up.

I can't believe I just did that, he thought. Some animal part of him had taken over. It all happened in a blur.

But now, one thing was clear above all. He knew what was coming next.

Dinner!

CHAPTER 6

Other than microwave popcorn, Vanessa had never been much of a cook. But since Carter had made the kill, and Buzz was keeping the fire, she volunteered to do something with the snake. She only wished she could have brought back some fish to go with it.

Everyone was so hungry, there was no talk of how disgusting this might have been in any other situation. Not even from Jane, who could barely stomach the snails. Now, even she was excited at the prospect of something new to eat.

The first thing they had to do was use a knife from the galley to cut off the snake's head. Jane said that if the snake was venomous, that's where the poison would be. She didn't know what kind of snake it was, but offered that it looked like a boa of some kind.

"Looks like snake steaks to me," Carter said, and pitched the severed head way back into the woods. "The rats can have that part."

With the head gone, Vanessa was surprised at how easily the skin came off. It was like peeling a sock away from a long tube. It made sense, actually. Snakes were built to shed.

After that, everyone agreed that it was best to slit the whole thing open and clean out the insides, the same way they'd seen Joe Kahali clean fish on the *Lucky Star*. For that, Vanessa took the snake and climbed down to the water's edge. After she'd sliced it along the belly, all the insides pulled out in one long, slimy piece. If she weren't so hungry, that part alone would have made her sick, Vanessa knew. It was amazing how easily it came to her now. She dropped the innards in the water without a thought and climbed back onto the deck with the snake meat dangling in her hand.

"Let's cook this thing," she said.

Buzz already had a pot heating over the campfire. The pot sat on a broken metal frame that Carter had torn out of the nav station for a cooking grate. The whole setup was kind of pathetic-looking and brilliant at the same time.

Vanessa cut the meat into small pieces so they'd cook quickly. Within a minute of dropping them into the hot pot, the smell reached her nostrils, and her mouth started to water.

As soon as the pieces felt firm to the touch, she passed one out to each of them. She blew on hers, trying to cool it, but quickly lost patience and popped the hot little nugget into her mouth.

The meat was chewy and full of tiny bones, but nobody cared about that. Even the flavor, like a cross between unsalted fish and dark-meat chicken, tasted as good as anything Vanessa had ever eaten.

For a long time, nobody said much. There was plenty to eat, and they all dipped back into the pot for another piece, and another, and another. Nobody even counted or kept track of who was getting how much. For once, it didn't matter.

Finally, Vanessa sat back, amazed at the tight feeling in her belly.

"I can't believe it," she said. "I'm full."

"Me, too," Buzz said. "When was the last time that happened?"

"Best. Snake. Ever!" Jane said.

And when everyone laughed, it was a little bit like getting dessert, too.

After the snake was gone, Buzz had one more idea for the day. He'd gathered up a few supplies, and now pulled them out of the wheelhouse.

"What are you doing?" Carter asked. He, Jane, and Vanessa were stretched out around the fire, keeping warm as the cool of the night came on. A chilly breeze from the ocean blew around the deck, and a sky full of stars had started to show overhead.

"I want to make a torch," Buzz said. "If I can."

He picked up a long thin piece of firewood and a bag of old oil-stained rags he'd found in the engine room. The rags hadn't seemed good for anything at first. Not until this idea had come to him.

He wrapped a thick, triple layer of material around the top of the stick. Then he bound it up with a long piece of wire he'd pulled out of a dead console in the wheelhouse. It worked like metal string, which was exactly what he needed.

"And now, the secret ingredient," he said, grinning at the others. He turned the would-be torch upside down and dipped it into a pot of the dark, oily sludge from the tank they'd found.

"How do you know that's going to burn?" Jane asked him.

"I don't," he said. He swirled the cotton rags around and around, getting them good and soaked.

"How do you know it won't explode?" Vanessa added.

Buzz shrugged. "I don't."

The others stood up and took several steps away. Buzz set the oil-soaked head of the torch on the ring of stones around the fire. Then he stepped back, too. Using another stick, he slowly pushed the torch toward the flames. Jane put her hands over her ears. Buzz squinted, waiting for whatever might come next.

The fire burned bright orange all around the rags, but nothing happened. Buzz pushed the torch farther into the fire and waited again. Then, with a hollow popping sound, the whole thing quietly burst into flame.

Carter, Jane, and Vanessa erupted in a cheer.

"Sweet!" Carter said.

Buzz was already feeling high after a full meal. Now, a wide grin spread across his face. He'd done it.

He reached over and took the torch by its handle, stood up with it, and stepped away from the campfire. It burned on its own beautifully—a bright yellow beacon against the dark sky.

This was amazing. It was like holding a giant flashlight. It was security on a dark night. It was *power*. Not just for him but for all of them. Already, Jane, Vanessa, and Carter were picking up sticks of their own and starting to assemble more of the homemade torches.

Within a few minutes, everyone had one. It felt like the Fourth of July, with a warm glow lighting the deck of the abandoned ship.

"Come on," Buzz said. "Let's test these things out."

"Where are you going?" Jane asked.

"For a walk."

Buzz went to the ship's rail and dropped his torch onto a dry patch of ground below. It hit the dirt and kept right on burning.

Soon all four of them were off the boat, headed toward the mouth of the cove. The torches lit the way as they climbed out onto the rocks to look at the endless stars and bright half-moon overhead.

Buzz could feel the warmth of the flames on his face. It was an amazing sensation—and, strangely, one of the most secure feelings he'd ever had.

"I think we can do this, you guys," he said.

"Do what?" Vanessa asked.

He gestured, sweeping his arm at the ocean, the shore, the cove—all of it.

"This," he said.

For a moment, no one said anything. They all

seemed to be taking in the power of the idea. They could do this. They *were* doing this.

Vanessa was the first to break the silence. "What do you think Dad and Beth would think if they could see us now?" she asked.

"You don't have to call her Beth," Jane said. "You can call her Mom. I bet she'd like that."

"I'll bet you're right," Vanessa said. For once, nobody seemed sad at the mention of their parents. "So what do you think Mom and Dad would think if they saw us now?"

"They'd think we were wild animals," Carter said, and let out a howl.

Then Buzz joined in. Jane and Vanessa, too. Soon, all four of them were laughing and baying at the moon, making as much noise as they pleased.

Why not? Buzz thought. This was *their* island, after all.

CHAPTER 7

When Carter woke up the next morning, rain was beating heavily against the cabin's porthole. That was no surprise. The weather changed all the time around here.

The surprise was that he could see daylight outside. Back at the old camp, sleeping in a cave at first, and then in their palm-and-bamboo shelter, none of them had ever gotten a full night's sleep. To actually wake up in the light, feeling rested, was amazing.

Now, Carter sat up and took a moment to check his hand. The cut from the base of the pinkie to his wrist was caked with dried blood. Even worse, it oozed yellow liquid around the edges. The hand itself was swollen, and he couldn't fully bend or straighten his fingers anymore. When he tried, the painful throb pulsed like a heartbeat in his hand.

Vanessa, Buzz, and Jane had all been telling him to keep the cut clean. But that was nearly impossible when your days were spent foraging in the jungle, cutting firewood, and moving all around an old, dirty ship. The sock he'd been using as a makeshift bandage had quickly grown so filthy, he'd thrown it away.

Carter stumbled out of the sleeping cabin and up the passageway to the center room outside the galley. Jane, Vanessa, and Buzz were sitting around the old wooden table, underneath the hatch that led up to the wheelhouse.

"Carter, your hand!" Vanessa said before he even spoke.

Carter shoved the hand into his pocket. He hadn't realized how obvious it would be.

"It feels fine," he said.

It was a lie, but if there was nothing they could do about it, there was no reason to worry everyone. They already had plenty to worry about. Vanessa narrowed her eyes at him, but Buzz spoke up before she could say anything else.

"We were talking about going to the old camp to get our stuff," Buzz said.

"Good idea," Carter said, glad for the change of subject. All of their things were still back there, including blankets, pillows, raincoats, and the axe.

"I think we should try to go through the woods," Vanessa said. "There's no way we can carry that stuff back over the rocks. And once we have a path, it'll probably be faster, too."

"The only question is whether we should wait for the rain to stop or just go," Jane said.

Carter looked at one of the dining hall portholes. It was so blurred with rain, he couldn't even see outside. Experience had shown them that this could be a passing shower, or it could continue all through the day.

"I say let's go for it," he said. "So we get wet, who cares? At least there's coconut back at camp."

"And coconut's way better than snails," Jane said.

Buzz nodded in agreement. "It's better than sitting around, too," he said.

That alone was a good enough reason to go, Carter thought. The hardest times here were at night, or whenever they stopped moving and working. That was when the dark thoughts tended to creep in the most.

"All right, it's decided then," Vanessa said, and stood up with the rest of them. "Let's go get wet."

The trip through the jungle was exactly as Jane expected. The rain poured down through the trees, and the ground was thick with mud in several places.

Even so, it was a shortcut compared to the rocky shoreline. Before long, they were slogging out of the woods and onto the beach they'd known as home base since crashing into the island a week ago.

There was no worrying about keeping dry anymore. In fact, being wet and muddy had become a badge of honor. It was how they lived here. They sat right down in the sand and opened two coconuts for a quick breakfast while the rain continued to fall.

As soon as they'd eaten, everyone agreed to gather up what they could, turn around, and head right back. Using their two blankets as packs, they piled in the axe, the sharp knife, the pillows, and all the remaining coconuts they could carry. There were four rain slickers as well, and everyone put one on.

Jane made sure to take the two pens she'd stashed between the rocks. Buzz took the little glass lens he used for making fire. He'd already found a substitute, but the old one was their good-luck charm, he said.

By the time they were loaded up and ready to go, the rain had gotten even worse. It poured down around them now like walls of water.

"Maybe we should wait," Jane said.

"Wait for what?" Carter asked.

Mother Nature had an answer for that question as she rocked the island with a massive bolt of lightning and a thunderous boom.

"What about the cave?" Jane asked.

"What about it?" Carter answered. "Remember

what happened the last time we used it to get out of a storm?"

Jane did remember. There was no forgetting that stampede of wild boars that had knocked her down—and very nearly done worse.

"If we're looking for shelter, so are they," Buzz added.

"Besides, Buzz already marked the trail," Vanessa said. "We can get back to the ship in fifteen minutes."

"But . . ." Jane started to protest, until she realized no one was listening anymore.

Carter slung one of the improvised blanket packs over his back. Vanessa took the other. Buzz carried the two coils of rope, one on each shoulder, and a pillowcase stuffed with silverware, socks, and some old sea charts from the *Lucky Star*.

Finally, Jane bent down and picked up the group's one backpack, filled with their water bottles, while the others glared at her impatiently.

They'd always babied her up till now, but not anymore. It didn't feel the way she'd always wanted it to, being treated just like anyone else. It felt scary.

But that was beside the point, wasn't it? Sometimes out here you had to accept what was and deal with it.

"Okay, I'm ready," Jane declared. "Let's go." She firmed her grip on the pack, wiped the rain out of her eyes, and started following the others back up into the woods.

CHAPTER 8

Mud sucked at Vanessa's feet as they made their way through the jungle. The heavy rain had turned the ground even muckier since they'd come through before. In the thickest patches, each step felt like lifting a heavy weight.

Their awkward load of supplies didn't help. It made maneuvering around the thick vines, over fallen trees, and under low branches that much more difficult. Several times, Vanessa had to stop and adjust the bundle on her back, or pick up something that had fallen out.

Buzz's blazed trail was the one thing that made the

going easier. He'd cut deep V-shaped gouges into the trees along the way, pointing them back toward the ship. Every ten or twenty yards, there was another blaze they could follow.

As they came onto a steep patch of ground where the land sloped toward the ocean, Vanessa stopped at the head of the line.

"What is that?" she asked, peering through the rain. Straight ahead, a heavy stream that hadn't been there before was washing downhill. It came from high on the slope to their left and continued all the way down to the ocean, somewhere off to the right. Most significantly, it ran directly across their path.

"Can we keep going?" Jane asked.

Buzz looked up and down the hill. "Do we have a choice?" he asked.

"We could go back if we have to," Vanessa said.

"And then what?" Carter said. "Carry all this stuff over the rocks? Leave it behind? I don't think so."

Nobody argued with that. Vanessa could tell they were all as anxious to reach the ship as she was.

"All right," she said. "Everyone hold on to each other. And be careful."

Vanessa took one end and locked arms with Buzz. He had Jane on the other side, with Carter at the opposite end. It was awkward going as they waded in, but it was better than trying to forge the gully separately. The water rushed by at a surprising speed, and the ground underneath was mush.

Vanessa lifted one foot and then the other, picking up her knees with each step. Her makeshift pack was soaked now and twice as heavy. She struggled to hold on to it with her outside hand.

"I don't know if I can carry this," she said.

"Just keep going," Carter said.

On the next step, Vanessa's foot landed in an unseen hole. Her leg sank deeper than ever, all the way up to her waist. When she tried to pull herself out, the mud at the bottom sucked her sneaker right off.

"Wait! I lost my shoe!" she yelled over the rain.

Buzz had been trying to keep hold of her arm, but now they'd been torn apart. Carter stumbled forward, too. He grasped his own pack with two hands and heaved it onto the ground at the far side of the gully. As soon as he did, he yelled out in pain and clutched his bad hand close to his chest.

"Carter? Are you okay?" Jane asked, but he didn't answer.

"Vanessa, here!" Buzz said, and reached to take her pack from her. As she handed it over, the knotted blanket came undone. One pillow and several precious coconuts washed downhill, immediately out of reach. Buzz threw the rest onto the bank.

"We have to go!" Jane yelled.

"I need my shoe!" Vanessa yelled back. She reached down, feeling for it, but found only handfuls of mud.

"It has to be there," Buzz said, his voice edged with impatience.

"I'm trying," Vanessa said. She knew they had to go, but a shoe wasn't something you could do without so easily around here.

Then, looking up, Vanessa saw something that erased all of her other concerns. A giant wall of mud had begun rolling downhill. It was headed toward them at an alarming rate.

"Vanessa!" Jane screamed. She'd seen it, too. Everyone had. Buzz started pulling on the group to get them going again.

"Leave the shoe!" he yelled. "Let's go!"

Vanessa couldn't move. She'd sunk too far now. She had no leverage to get herself out of the hole anymore. Buzz was straining, pulling on her arm, getting nowhere. Carter tried for her, but his hand was just out of reach.

They were running out of time, and the earth itself, it seemed, was pouring down in their direction.

Jane screamed.

"Watch out!" she yelled. Before she could move out of the way, a heavy wave of earth, mud, water, and debris smashed into them. She was caught in it now. They all were. The last she saw of the others, Vanessa's head had disappeared under the deluge, and Carter had lunged for the bank. She saw Buzz fall sideways, carried downhill by the mud itself.

It was the same for her. Everything was a blur at first, and then dark. There was no controlling her movement, or the direction in which she traveled. She tumbled along, as if in slow motion, half buried by the sludge.

Unseen rocks and roots thumped at her body. The trees on either side seemed to be traveling in the opposite direction. She reached for the bank, but it was impossible to move toward it.

Her mind raced. Would she be dumped into the ocean to drown? Buried alive? There was no knowing where this was taking her, or what would happen before it was over.

The mudslide had her, and there was nothing she could do about it.

Buzz couldn't see. He couldn't hear. He could only feel himself sliding downhill, carried along beyond his own control.

But then he sensed a change. The flow slowed. The

earth around him seemed to churn, and then came to a stop. It left him suspended where he was like any other piece of debris in the muck.

Muscles straining, Buzz struggled to get free. First, he managed to come onto his knees. He wiped away what he could from his eyes and then lunged toward the nearest bank. He was crawling more than walking, but it got him up onto higher ground.

Standing on shaky legs, he looked around.

"Vanessa!" he screamed. "Jane! Carter! Where are you?"

He'd lost all track of them. He had no idea if they were uphill, downhill, or still buried under the river of mud.

The first one he saw was Carter, lying on the same side of the gully, twenty or thirty yards uphill. He was on his back, panting heavily with his hand clutched to his chest.

"Vanessa! Jane!" Buzz yelled again.

"I'm here!" Jane's voice came from somewhere below. Buzz looked, but he couldn't see her through the woods.

"Are you okay?" Carter yelled.

"I . . . I think so," Jane called back. "I'm coming up."

"Where's Vanessa?" Buzz asked. His heart thumped like a fist in his chest. "Carter, do you see her?"

Carter sat up to look around. "No!" he called.

The last Buzz had seen Vanessa, she was stuck in a hole, somewhere uphill of this spot, but nothing looked familiar anymore. The mudslide had completely disoriented him.

He worked his way higher, struggling to hurry. With the heavy mud on his arms, legs, and clothes, he felt as if he were running underwater.

"Vanessa!" he yelled again.

And then he saw her. Vanessa's arm was sticking out of the mud in the middle of the gully, reaching and flailing for something to grab on to. The rest of her was completely submerged.

"Get her!" Carter shouted. Jane was coming up behind them now, and they rushed toward the spot.

How much time had passed? One minute? Two minutes? All Buzz knew right now was that Vanessa was still moving. And he had to get her out, whatever it took.

Without hesitation, he launched himself back into the gully. Quickly, the mud was past his knees and putting a hard grip on him. Another few steps and he'd be part of the problem instead of the solution.

But Vanessa was still out of reach. Panic was setting in. It was hard to think of what to do.

"Buzz, she's going to suffocate!" Jane yelled.

"No, she's not!" Buzz said. There was no way he'd let his sister go down like this. It wasn't going to happen. The truth of it burned into his gut. "Get me something!" he yelled back. "The axe, or a branch—anything!"

Jane and Carter were on it right away. "Here!" Jane handed him a long crooked branch. It whipped Buzz in the face as he turned to take it, but he barely noticed.

He reached out now, swinging the tree limb in Vanessa's direction.

"Vanessa! HERE!" he yelled as loudly as he could. Whether or not she could hear him, he had no idea. Her hand swung from side to side, sweeping the air until it finally struck the branch. Then her fingers closed around it.

"Now pull!" Carter said to Buzz from behind. Buzz could feel Jane's and Carter's hands around his waist, yanking on him and doing what they could to help.

Vanessa held tightly to the opposite end of the branch, but the suction of the mud was so tight, it threatened to pull Buzz in after her. He dug his heels into the sludge and held on. Then he managed a single step back. Then another.

Slowly, the top of Vanessa's head emerged. Her other arm came out of the muck, and she grabbed the branch with both hands now. Buzz gripped his end as hard as he could, while Jane and Carter guided him backward. When he hit the bank, he stumbled and fell right onto Jane.

As Vanessa's head cleared the mud, her face was still completely covered. Her lips parted, and she took a huge gasp of air, even as more mud dropped into her mouth. She spit and coughed, then spit again, and finally took a full breath. Buzz leaned forward and grabbed on to her as she clawed her way toward the bank.

Finally, he fell back again, catching his own breath. His strength was gone, his muscles like rubber. He'd poured out everything he'd had, and then some. But everyone was safe now. That's what mattered most.

When he looked up, Vanessa was still sheathed in mud. The skin on her face was sagging under the weight. She looked eighty years old, at least.

And Buzz started to laugh. He couldn't help it. His thirteen-year-old sister looked more like their great-grandma Diaz than herself right now.

"What are you laughing at?" Vanessa gasped out.

Buzz put his arms around her and let the rain pour down, washing them clean.

"Nothing," he said. "I'm just glad you're okay."

"I lost my shoe," Vanessa said weakly.

That only made Buzz laugh harder. He couldn't stop. It wasn't just the shoe. It was the sense of relief. For a moment, he'd thought they might actually lose Vanessa. And that had been too much to bear.

Finally, they stood up again and started gathering what they could. Buzz threw several provisions into one of their soaking-wet blankets, tied it into a bundle,

and picked it up, feeling ready to get back to the ship once and for all.

He turned to where Carter had been standing and doing nothing for the last minute. "Can you take this?" Buzz asked, holding out the bundle for him.

Carter nodded, reached for it, and then dropped the pack as soon as he tried to take it.

"Carter?" Jane said. "What's wrong?"

Carter's expression was a twist of pain. "My hand," he said. It was bleeding again. His fingers were curled and swollen, and his face was pale as he looked around at the group. "I don't think I can use it anymore."

CHAPTER 9

July 9. Day 11 on Nowhere Island. Two weeks(!!) since we left Hawaii.

Dear Mom and Dad,

It seems like forever since I saw you. I know these letters aren't real, but I like writing them anyway.

It's been three days since the mudslide, and we haven't been able to get back to the old camp since then. Not even along the rocks.

The problem is, our old beach is where the coconuts grow. We've been all over the woods around here and haven't found a single one. No other fruit, no nuts, no nothing. Not even another snake. The one thing we have left to eat here is snails. And you know how I feel about those! Still, I eat them, and it feels like nothing in my stomach. You should see how different we all look now. I think maybe we're starting to starve, for real.

Vanessa's working really hard trying to catch fish, but I don't think they want to be caught. She thinks maybe if we build a raft, we can get out to the reef and find more of them there. So far, we've cut down a bunch of bamboo from the woods (too bad we can't eat bamboo), and we work on the raft a little bit every day. It's hard to get much done with just a few snails for breakfast, lunch, and dinner.

I know we'll figure something out, but I really (really, REALLY) wish we would hurry up and do it. All we think about is food these days. I shouldn't even be writing this right now. I should be getting ready to go out into the woods and start looking before the sun gets too high.

Maybe this will be our lucky morning. I hope so.

Miss you, love you,

xoxoxoxo to infinity,

Jane

Buzz knelt down next to Carter's bunk and put a hand on his arm. Carter's skin was hot to the touch. He definitely had a fever, and he'd been sleeping more than anyone.

"Carter?" Buzz shook him gently. "We're going out scavenging. Can you come up and watch the fire?"

Carter stirred and came half awake. "I wanna come hunting," he slurred.

"We need someone to watch the fire," Buzz repeated. It wasn't totally true. On a sunny day like this one, Buzz could easily use his little glass lens to restart the fire. In fact, he'd gotten really good at it. But everyone agreed that Carter needed to rest as much as possible.

Carter sat up and stretched. "I'll go out and get some wood, at least," he said.

"Already did it," Buzz told him. "There's a ton of it in the wheelhouse. Just make sure the fire doesn't go out. There's a bucket of oil up there, too, if you need it. And I left some water. Make sure you drink a lot."

It was strange, telling Carter what to do. Not that long ago, it had been the other way around most of the time.

But Carter didn't argue. "I'll be right there," he said.

Buzz left him in the cabin and walked up the passage to the middle deck's central room. From there, he climbed onto the table, stepped onto the steel trunk they'd found in one of the cabins, and climbed up through the hatch to the wheelhouse above. It was enough of a makeshift stairs that even Carter could do it with one hand. But for how much longer, Buzz wasn't sure. That hand wasn't getting any better. The only thing they could do now was try to get some food into Carter, to keep up his strength.

And *that* was proving harder than anyone had thought it would be.

Inside the wheelhouse, Buzz picked up the axe and the backpack they used for scavenging. The pack was loaded with a sharp knife, a length of rope, and two empty bottles they'd fill at the stream on their way out.

Stepping outside, he could see Jane down by the water's edge, writing in her journal. Vanessa was there, too, looking down at a row of bamboo she'd been trying to puzzle into a raft.

And out by the ocean, at the mouth of the cove, Buzz could see their new signal fire. He liked looking at it. It was the one thing that had come together well in the last three days. The tall tepee-shaped pyre of wood and kindling was similar to the signal they'd had on Lookout Point. It didn't have the advantage of being up high like the last one, but if another plane or a ship came by, they could at least get to this one to light it in a matter of seconds.

"You guys ready to go?" Buzz called down to the girls.

Jane stood up and closed her journal. "What are we looking for today?" she asked.

"Cheeseburgers," Vanessa answered. It was a daily joke now. The day before it had been pizza, and the day before that, chocolate cake.

"Think we'll find any?" Vanessa added.

"Probably," Buzz said. "But we'd better get moving before they run out."

Vanessa led Jane and Buzz into the woods, hacking at anything that stood in their way. It wasn't necessary to take out quite so much brush, but the entire jungle was getting on her nerves today.

The air here was a thick stew of humidity and stillness. It was like breathing through a wet washcloth. The shoes she'd borrowed from Carter for the morning were too tight, and the mosquitoes were always terrible in the woods. She didn't even bother trying to wave them off anymore. There was no point.

She stopped and scanned the area, hoping for a flash of color that might turn out to be something edible. Bananas would have been amazing, or papaya, or mango, or any of the other things Jane said grew in this part of the world. Even coconut or another snake would have been more than welcome. But so far all they'd brought back from these morning hikes was firewood and kindling.

"Can we burn this?" Jane's voice came from the other side of a scraggly thicket.

"What is it?" Vanessa asked. She ducked under a tangle of vines and worked her way over to where Buzz and Jane were looking down at a large dead tree on the ground.

"We could get a lot of firewood out of this," Jane said.

"Does rotten wood burn?" Vanessa asked. She put one foot on the tree and buried the axe blade into its bark three times. On each swing, it landed with a soft thud that didn't sound too encouraging. The wood only broke open and fell apart where she tried to cut it.

"Come on, let's keep going," Vanessa said.

"Wait!" Buzz said. The excitement in his voice stopped her. She turned back to see him kneeling right on top of the tree.

"What is it?"

"Jane, hand me the knife," Buzz said. Already, he was picking through the crumbly bark with his fingers. Jane opened the pack on his back and handed him a six-inch serrated blade. He took it and plunged the tip into the soft wood, working the knife around in circles to open up a hole.

Whatever Buzz was doing, Vanessa could see he was onto something. His eyes were still and focused, his mouth set in a frozen line of concentration. Before Nowhere Island, the only time she'd seen that expression was when Buzz sat on the couch at home, deep inside a game of FarQuest or Reverb Alley.

"What are you doing?" Vanessa asked.

"I thought I saw a grub," Buzz said.

"A what?"

He withdrew the knife now and stuck two fingers inside. When he pulled them out, he had a pinch hold on a lumpy white worm the size of his pinkie.

Buzz dropped it onto his palm and held the thing out to show them. "These little suckers are pure protein," he said.

Jane leaned in to see. "We're supposed to eat *those*?" she asked.

"I'm not saying they're candy bars," Buzz told her. "I'm just saying they're edible. And there's probably a lot more of them here, too."

The grub was more like a caterpillar than a worm, Vanessa realized. It had a shiny dark head at one end and tiny legs that sent it wriggling across Buzz's palm. Snails were one thing, but the grub was ten times as big and probably twice as disgusting.

Her empty stomach seemed to fold in on itself. She knew exactly what she had to do, and she didn't like the answer one bit. It was another *island moment*. That's how Vanessa thought of them now.

She was going to eat grubs. Not because she liked

them. Not because she thought it would be fun. But simply because there was one thing about them that mattered more than anything else.

They were edible.

CHAPTER 10

Carter startled himself awake.

He'd been dreaming—about what, he wasn't even sure. Something had been chasing him. Something getting closer. Reaching out to grab him. And then—

He sat up on the deck, breathing heavily and remembering where he was. This fever wasn't doing him any favors—that was for sure.

The campfire had burned down while he slept. Its embers were still bright orange, but he needed to feed it soon if he didn't want to lose it. With Buzz, Vanessa, and Jane off sweating in the jungle, it was the very least he could do.

Carter shuffled across the deck and into the wheelhouse for more of the dry wood Buzz had stacked there. His bad hand was swollen stiff, but he could still grip certain things like pieces of firewood, as long as they weren't too small. He bent down, grabbed an armload, and stood up.

His head swam. The room started spinning. Carter dropped the wood, leaned against the wall, and slid back down to the floor.

Tears squeezed out from the corners of his eyes. Even standing too fast was a problem. It was beyond frustrating. When they'd landed on the island, he had been the strong one. He had been the one they could all count on to get the most done. But not anymore.

Without thinking, he pounded the steel deck with his bad hand. It sent a nauseating bolt of pain up his arm, and he screamed—as much from the frustration as anything else. He took up a piece of the firewood with his good hand and flung it as hard as he could, not caring where it went.

A small crash sounded from the other side of the room, followed by the sound of broken glass falling onto the floor. Carter looked over to see a row of framed photographs above the wheelhouse windows. Two of them were smashed, their frames splintered at the corners.

He'd walked by those photos a hundred times without ever really noticing them. Now he saw that they were fishing pictures. In one, several men were casting off the back of a boat. In another, someone stood on a dock next to an enormous swordfish.

It was a painful reminder of Carter's own empty belly and everything he hadn't been able to accomplish here. He picked up another piece of wood and took out two more of the photos with one throw.

For a long time, Carter didn't move. The anger that coursed through him was a paralyzing feeling. His muscles and his mind seemed locked up together inside of it. And who was there to blame for all this? *No one.* Not even himself.

They'd done nothing wrong. This was all supposed to have been a fun sailing trip, a week on the boat with Uncle Dexter. Their parents thought it would be a chance for the four kids to get to know one another better, as brothers and sisters. Now, here they were, fighting for their lives instead. And it sure didn't feel like a fair fight.

Slowly, Carter's thoughts evened out. He remembered what he had to do. He took his time standing up, gathered another armload of wood, and headed for the door.

He was nearly outside when he stopped again. Something about the fishing photos had caught his attention. One of them was different than the others, and he stepped back for a closer look.

The picture was an underwater shot. It showed a man in swim trunks, holding a spear of some kind. Instead of gripping the spear near the base like a regular weapon, the man held it near the barbed tip, with a long strap stretched all the way along its length. The whole thing seemed to be cocked like a slingshot, ready to fire.

It was nothing Carter had ever seen before, but as he looked at it, the spear made perfect sense. Vanessa had been talking about making a raft to get them out to the reef for fishing. It was a good idea, but what if they could get *down* to the reef as well? That's where the fish really were, after all.

Carter went outside and stoked the campfire, then jumped off the ship and headed straight up into the jungle. Vanessa had been harvesting bamboo for the raft, and he went right to the grove she'd told him about.

When he got there, he scouted out a long thin piece. It was nearly six feet high where it grew. Perfect for what he had in mind. Using his good hand he grabbed hold of the cane, angled his foot against the base, and snapped it free.

Back at the ship, he reentered the wheelhouse. There, he turned his attention to the row of windows at the front of the room. Most of them had broken or missing glass, but they all still had the black rubber weather stripping that ran around their frames. When he poked at the material with his finger, it seemed spongy, and maybe even stretchy enough for the job. He reached up and peeled away one of the strips, being careful to keep it all in one piece.

Already, Carter felt completely exhausted. He knew

he didn't have much more in him, but he wanted to get this done.

With the bamboo wedged between his knees, he looped one end of the rubber strip around its base and used his teeth to grab the other end, cinching it tight. He repeated the process, tying it off with one of the knots Uncle Dexter had taught him on board the *Lucky Star*. Now he had a big lasso of rubber attached to the end of his would-be spear.

There was just one more step, maybe the most important one. He grabbed one of the sharp knives and whittled away the tip of the bamboo until he'd created a strong, sharp point.

Even in his feverish state, Carter felt just a little bit better. The others had been working hard while he'd slept next to the fire. But now, in less than half an hour, with just the materials he had on hand, he'd worked up a pretty good fishing spear. It was simple and crude, but if it worked, it would change everything. They wouldn't have to starve, because they'd be drowning in fish.

The only thing left to do was test it out. But not

right now. As much as he wanted to keep going, Carter's swimming head and fuzzy thoughts told him otherwise. Reluctantly, he took some more wood out to the fire and lay down to close his eyes for a quick rest.

Just a few minutes, Carter thought. Then he'd be right back at it.

When Buzz got back to the ship with the girls, Carter was up on the main deck, dozing next to the campfire. It looked as if he hadn't moved from his spot in hours.

He sat up and rubbed his eyes as they all set down their armloads of fresh firewood.

"Any luck?" Carter asked.

"Well, the good news is, we found something to eat," Buzz said.

"What's the bad news?"

Buzz reached into his pocket and set down a handful of grubs.

"Say hello to our lunch."

Vanessa laughed nervously, Jane didn't say a word, and Carter leaned in for a better look. There were eighteen of them in all. A few of the grubs had died on the way, but most of them were wriggling around, trying to get back on their feet.

Buzz plopped down next to Carter, as did Jane and Vanessa.

"What are they?" Carter asked.

"You mean besides totally disgusting?" Jane asked. "They're grubs. Buzz says they're pure protein."

Buzz couldn't help feeling a little proud. Maybe the grubs *were* the grossest possible food source, but it was better than the alternative: no food at all.

"Who wants to go first?" he asked.

"I think you do," Vanessa said.

It was hard to argue with that. "Yeah, all right," he said. He picked one up and stared at it. The grub fidgeted back and forth between his fingers.

This is food, he told himself. *Nutrition. Protein. The stuff my body needs.*

Before he could think about it another second, he stuck the whole thing in his mouth and bit down hard. It sent a thick greenish liquid spilling over his lips and down his chin.

"EWWWW!" all three of the others groaned at once.

"*That* . . . is the grossest thing I've ever seen," Jane said.

Buzz knew he couldn't stop now. He tilted his head back, fighting the urge to spit the whole thing out. The grub tasted like dirt and chemicals. It didn't help that it was so chunky, either. But he kept on chewing, as fast as he could.

Finally, with one very hard gulp, it went down. He opened his mouth and stuck out his tongue to show he'd done it.

"I can't believe you just ate that," Carter said.

"It wasn't so bad," Buzz lied, and downed half a bottle of water to wash away the taste. He could still feel bits and pieces on his tongue, but he tried not to think about that. "Who's next?" he asked.

"Go ahead, Vanessa," Carter said. "I dare you."

"I dare *you*," Vanessa said.

Carter picked up two of the grubs and held them out on his palm.

"Let's race," he said.

Vanessa grinned uneasily as she took one from him. "Yeah, all right."

"Ready?" Jane asked. "One . . . two . . . three!"

Buzz watched as Vanessa tossed the grub onto her tongue, clapped both hands over her mouth, and started chewing.

"Carter!" Jane said. "That's even . . . grosser!"

When Buzz looked over, Carter was unclenching his fist. His hand was covered in pieces of squished grub and the greenish liquid. He held it up to his mouth, scraped the mess off with his teeth, and swallowed it all in one pass.

"Hey!" Vanessa said. "That's not fair!"

"Says who?" Carter asked. As if to make his point, he scooped up a second grub, squeezed it into a mush, and got it down before Vanessa had finished her first. All without a sip of water.

It wasn't such a bad idea, Buzz thought. At least it got rid of the need for any chewing. He picked one up for himself, closed his eyes, and squeezed. A soft, warm goo filled his hand, but he didn't look at it. He kept his eyes closed and downed the whole thing as quickly as possible. His stomach churned as he reached for the water bottle.

Vanessa was still struggling with her first one, but now that she'd started, she seemed determined to get through her share. She took a swig of water, picked up another grub, and kept going.

The whole time, Jane watched them as if she were sitting in front of a horror movie. Her hands never came down from her mouth, until finally, she scooted forward and looked down at the remaining wriggling grubs on the deck.

"What do you think, Jane?" Carter asked. His grin showed several little legs still stuck in his teeth, but he didn't seem to mind. In fact, the change in him was amazing. With even just a tiny bit of food, he was more alert than he'd been all day.

"Mom always says you should try everything once," he added. "I'll even mash it up for you."

"Don't bother," Jane said. She took a thin stick from the pile of kindling near the fire. Then she skewered three grubs, one by one, and held them over the glowing embers to roast. They looked like the world's ugliest marshmallows.

Buzz glanced at Carter and Vanessa, who looked back at him. It wasn't the first time Jane had proven herself to be the smartest one in the group.

Soon, everyone had a skewer going. Green liquid dripped and sizzled into the fire while the grubs roasted away. Buzz wasn't convinced this would make them taste any better, but one thing was for sure. They couldn't taste any worse.

"Good idea, Janie," Vanessa said.

"I'm going to pretend it's cooked fish," Jane said grimly. "And I don't even like fish."

"Oh—I almost forgot!" Carter said suddenly. He handed his skewer to Vanessa and walked toward the wheelhouse.

"Where are you going?" Vanessa called out.

"I have something to show you guys," he said. "I'll be right back."

As soon as Carter came out of the wheelhouse carrying his invention, Jane knew what it was.

"That's a Hawaiian sling!" she said. She abandoned

her skewer of grubs and went over for a closer look.

"It's just a spear," Carter said.

"Yeah—a *fishing* spear," she said. "Why didn't you tell us?"

Her brother shrugged. "I was pretty out of it when you got here."

"How does it work?" Vanessa asked.

Carter held up the black-and-white photograph he'd found and passed it around.

"Ohh," Buzz said, looking at the photo. "Sling, like slingshot. I get it."

He fitted the lasso around his elbow and pulled the bamboo shaft back until he was holding the spear close to the tip, like the man in the picture. The rubber loop stretched tight along its length.

Next, he moved over to the ship's rail and took aim. "Be careful!" Vanessa said, just before the spear sprang out of his hand. The whole thing flew toward the beach and stuck in the sand several inches deep. For a piece of bamboo and rubber, the force was impressive.

"Sweet!" Buzz said. "I think this could work."

"Yeah, and no more grubs," Jane said.

"Nice job, Carter," Vanessa told him.

"*Really* nice job," Buzz added.

When Jane looked over, there was something different in Buzz's expression. It was no secret he'd always been jealous of Carter, the jock of the family. But all Jane saw on Buzz's face now was admiration.

And when the two boys traded a fist bump, she knew for sure that something had changed between them. It was as if they'd forgotten they didn't like each other. Maybe that made them friends, and maybe it didn't, but they were definitely turning into brothers out here.

She just wished Mom and Dad were around to see it.

CHAPTER 11

Vanessa's hands shook. It was still early morning, but she'd been up since first light, getting the raft ready to go once and for all. For the last hour or more, that had meant tying dozens of knots to bind the bamboo pieces together as snugly as her strength would allow.

Maybe it was the hunger giving her the shakes. Or maybe it was excitement at the prospect of real food for the family. She'd been inspired by Carter's fishing spear and had barely gotten any sleep thinking about it. If they could just get out on the water, she felt sure they could catch some fish.

Now, with the morning sun shining straight back into the cove, Vanessa made a final check of her work. The raft was finished. It looked like a version of the shelter roof they'd built back at the old beach, just a dozen bamboo poles lashed side by side. It wasn't so much to look at, but the real question was, Would it do the job?

Vanessa's tired muscles drove a little harder as she dragged the raft into the shallow water at the edge of the cove. It floated there, perfectly. That part was no surprise. The bamboo was incredibly buoyant. But it would have to hold their weight, too.

She waded out a little farther and pushed down on the raft with both hands. The bamboo poles clacked against each other and sprang back easily each time.

More importantly, the raft held together as she climbed on board. With a couple of homemade paddles, it was more than enough to get them out to the reef. It would be like having their own movable diving platform.

"Is that our new raft?" Jane's voice came from the direction of the ship.

Vanessa turned to see her standing at the rail.

"Sure is," she said. "Get Buzz and come on down. We're going out fishing!"

───────

Carter didn't ask anyone's permission to come along that morning. There was no way he'd be staying back while everyone else did all the work. Not again.

"What about your hand?" Vanessa asked as he climbed onto the raft next to Jane.

"What about it?" Carter said. He picked up one of the two paddles Buzz had made. It was a thick piece of bamboo split down the middle, and the curve of it fit right into the C-shape of his stiff, swollen fingers.

"See? I can even paddle," he said. "It's not like my arms and legs are broken."

"I don't know, Carter," Vanessa said warily.

"You don't have to," he said. "Because I'm not asking."

He expected more of an argument, but Vanessa simply shook her head and set the Hawaiian sling on the raft. Jane took up the second paddle. Buzz had a cloth bag made out of his own shirt, and he tied it to his belt loop with a piece of rope. With any luck, that bag would be heavy with fish by the time they got back. It was time to go.

Carter's head still swam with fever, but he wasn't going to let that stop him. He knew exactly where he wanted to be.

"Let's get going," he said. "The sooner we get out there, the sooner we eat!"

"I hear that," Buzz said, and they pushed off.

The day was calm and windless. Jane and Carter paddled while Vanessa and Buzz stayed in the water, flutter-kicking off the back like a human outboard motor. It all made for easy going as they worked their way past the mouth of the cove and into the open water just off the shore of Nowhere Island.

Looking back, Carter got a view he hadn't had before. The island's cliffs looked even huger from here. It was hard to believe they'd climbed down those rock walls just a few days earlier.

It was also hard to believe that this place was

uncharted, and that nobody had put it on a map by now. But the fact was, there were ten thousand miles of Pacific Ocean all around them. However big the island looked, it was a needle in a watery haystack.

As they paddled farther out, several white blobs with long, thin tentacles passed by the raft on either side. They looked to Carter like half-inflated balloons.

"Jellyfish!" Jane said, pointing down at them.

"Are they edible?" Carter asked, ready to scoop one up with his paddle.

"I don't think so," Jane answered. "In fact, they might be the stinging kind. We should keep moving."

Soon the wide coral reef came into view. The turquoise water here was like wavy glass. Carter could see the colored shapes of fish—*edible* fish—darting in and out of the coral. It looked like a little underwater city. A busy one, too. That was encouraging.

"This is the spot!" Vanessa called out. "Hey, Carter, hand me the sling."

There was no question about who would be going down for the fish. Carter's injured hand and fever meant he was already doing everything he could.

Buzz wasn't much of a diver. And Jane had tried to use the spear, but it was just too big for her.

"Wish me luck," Vanessa said.

"Good luck," Carter said, along with Jane and Buzz at the same time.

Vanessa took three breaths and held the last one. Then she flashed a thumbs-up, flipped over in the water with the spear at her side, and headed down.

CHAPTER 12

As Vanessa made her way down to the reef, it was like escaping from one world into another. Unlike the rest of the island, this place was cool, wet, and amazingly quiet.

A mask and fins would have been a big help, but the water was like crystal. Also, unlike the last time, when they'd dived down to the sunken *Lucky Star*, the reef here was just a short drop from the surface. It took only a few seconds to reach it.

Fish scattered as Vanessa came near but quickly worked their way back in her direction. She saw blurred flashes of color everywhere. A yellow, black, and white fish swam right in front of her. Another, the same blue-green as a tropical parrot, darted between two branches of coral. A school of tiny silver ones flitted by.

This place was like a grocery store, she thought. Time to start shopping.

It wasn't easy, though. It took several trips down, then back up for air, just to get an idea of where the biggest concentration of fish was.

On her fourth dive, Vanessa started figuring out how to stop and float in one position, rather than shooing the fish away with too much movement.

The next time, she started thinking more about the spear. She kept it ready now, held out in front of her with the sling pulled tight.

After each trip down, her technique had improved. On the sixth, seventh, and eighth dives, she managed to get off actual shots at actual fish—but missed every time. Still, the adrenaline of the hunt was enough to keep her going.

On the ninth try, Vanessa swam down to her favorite spot alongside the brown-green wall of coral.

She leveled her body in the water, parallel to the sandy bottom, and floated there, waiting for as long as her lungs would allow.

Out of the coral, a flat, pale-pink-and-white fish the size of her hand nosed forward. It paused to nibble something off the reef, just a few feet away.

Vanessa knew this was the one. She could feel it in her bones before she even fired.

Sling cocked, she released her grip on the shaft and let it fly. It zipped through the water and at nearly the same moment found its mark. The fish shimmied violently back and forth on the tip of the spear, but it had no chance of getting away.

Vanessa let out an underwater scream. "YES!" she cried, sending a stream of bubbles toward the surface. She'd done it. She'd caught her first fish. And this wasn't *just* a fish. This was the beginning of something that could help save their lives.

Keeping a grip on the spear, she turned and kicked her way back toward the raft. She held the fish overhead so it would be the first thing Carter, Jane, and Buzz saw coming out of the water.

But there was no need. Even before she reached the top, she could hear them up there, already screaming for joy.

But there was no need. Even before she reached the top, she could hear them up there, already screaming for joy.

For a long time, Buzz hung out on the raft with Jane and Carter while Vanessa made one trip down after another. She was like a machine, and it wasn't hard to see why. Every fourth or fifth dive, she managed to come up with something else on her spear. The bag hanging off Buzz's belt loop was so heavy with fish by now, it made his mouth water.

A week ago, they'd been living in a cave, with nothing. Now, they had a dry shelter, a constant source of water, and—finally—an endless supply of food. Was it better than being back home? Not in a million years. But it *was* a million times better than it had been.

As Vanessa surfaced once more, Buzz rolled over to see a little brown and green speckled fish flicking on the sharpened point of her bamboo spear.

"That's five!" she said. "Let's go for one more."

"Up to you," Buzz told her. They already had enough for a meal, but then again, more was more. He lifted the slippery fish off the spear with both hands, being careful not to drop it. Jane held the bag open for him, and he turned to put the fish inside.

As he did, a ripple of movement off to the side caught Buzz's eye.

"I'm going down again," Vanessa said behind him.

"Hold on," Buzz said. The bamboo dug into his knees as he came up higher for a better look.

"What is it?" Jane asked.

"I don't know."

Buzz stared off to the right, his pulse ticking upward. The glinting sun on the water made it hard to see, but *something* was definitely moving toward them. Not a fish. Not a little one, anyway. It was some kind of big, dark shape.

And then, as a triangular gray fin broke the surface, his worst fear was confirmed all at once.

"Vanessa, get up here. *Now!*" he said.

Vanessa didn't question it. She threw the spear

onto the raft and started scrambling on board.

"Carter, wake up!" Jane said, shaking him out of his nap.

"What's going on?" Carter asked.

There was no time to answer. The raft shimmied hard and tilted under Vanessa's weight, throwing Buzz off balance. He reached for an edge, or anything to hold on to, but it was no good. As the others scrabbled toward the middle of the raft, it was already breaking apart underneath them. Jane fell in first. Buzz tried to grab her, but his legs slid between two of the bamboo poles. The gap between them yawned open, and he slipped right through into the ocean. The yell that came out of him quickly turned into a mouthful of seawater. Then a lungful, too.

He choked and coughed under the surface. Sections of bamboo floated free over his head, creating shadows in the water that only confused him more. Twisting around, Buzz tried to spot the oncoming shark, wherever it was. His hand curled into a fist, a pathetic defense against an unbeatable predator.

From behind him, it whizzed by. Buzz flinched hard,

fully expecting the shock of a bite somewhere—his arm, his leg. But no. The thing kept right on moving. All Buzz saw was a receding blue-gray blur.

He popped up to the surface where Jane, Vanessa, and Carter were churning the water as well, all of them struggling to get out of the way. The bag of fish still hung from his belt loop and twisted awkwardly around his legs. He realized it probably made him a floating piece of bait, but he couldn't let the fish go—not even now.

It took some number of endless panic-filled seconds to realize the shark was gone, or at least out of sight. But that didn't stop the five-alarm dose of adrenaline that was still running through Buzz's system.

"Let's get out of here!" he yelled. Everyone grabbed a piece of raft and started kicking toward the shore as fast as they could.

It was only as they were underway that Buzz noticed a sharp stinging pain in his leg. He wasn't sure if it had just happened, or if it had been there all along behind the rush of confusion. But now, it was impossible to ignore. A searing hot tingle ran up from his calf, through his upper leg, and into his entire body.

"You guys, I think I got bit!" he said.

"What?" Vanessa asked. She let go of her own piece of bamboo and swam over to reach Buzz's. "Where'd it get you?"

Buzz reached down and touched the spot on his calf where the pain had started. There was no blood, at least none he could see. But it was hard to tell with all the movement around him. One thing he knew about sharks above all—they could smell tiny amounts of blood over huge distances of water.

"There's nothing we can do out here. Can you make it back?" Vanessa asked.

Buzz only nodded. There was no choice, but the pain and the panic were nearly overwhelming. It was all he could do to kick toward the shore—and pray that he didn't see any signs of a return visit.

As soon as they reached the mouth of the cove, Jane worked with Carter and Vanessa to help Buzz up onto the rocks at the shoreline. His face had gone pale, and his jaw was set in a constant grimace of pain.

Vanessa knelt next to him. "Where does it hurt?" she asked.

"All over," Buzz groaned, and squeezed his eyes shut.

"Where'd you get bit?" Jane asked.

He pointed to his left calf, where an angry red blotch showed on the skin. There were no teeth marks or punctures. Just some kind of raised rash.

"I think that's a jellyfish sting," Jane said. "I'll bet anything."

She pointed at the spot, and Buzz raised his head to see. He nodded in agreement and then lay back again.

"What can we do?" Carter asked.

"I don't know!" Vanessa said.

"You have to . . . pee . . . on it," Buzz gritted out.

"He's right!" Jane said, and looked straight at Carter. "I've heard about this. Peeing on it gets rid of the pain."

"What?" Carter asked. "What do you mean, pee?"

"Like, urinate," Jane said.

"I know what *pee* means, Jane. I'm just asking—"

"JUST DO IT!" Buzz said, with as much force as Jane had ever heard from him.

If anyone was going to do this, it had to be Carter. That went without saying. But Carter wasn't looking so good himself. He'd overdone it—Jane could tell with a glance. He was hunched over with his hands on his knees, as though he were struggling to keep to his feet.

"Okay," he said into the ground. "I've got this."

Without being asked, Jane and Vanessa looked away. Jane squeezed Vanessa's hand and watched the water. It was hard, knowing Buzz was in so much pain, and to hear him groaning there on the rocks.

"Could you hurry up already?" Buzz said behind her.

"I'm working on it," Carter said.

"Just do it. And don't pee on the fish!"

"Just shut up, okay?"

There was a long, silent pause. When Buzz spoke

again, Jane could hear that some of the tension had already left his voice. It sounded as if the peeing had actually worked, and quickly, too.

"By the way, this never happened," Buzz said.

"You're telling me," Carter added, zipping up his shorts.

Jane bit her lip to stop from laughing and kept her eyes on the water. She could see a few loose pieces of bamboo floating out by the reef. One of the paddles was in sight, but the other was gone, along with the Hawaiian sling. They'd have to start all over on a new raft, but at least they still had the fish.

"Hey!" Vanessa shouted out. "It's back!"

Jane turned to look where Vanessa was pointing. A gray fin was just slipping beneath the water's surface. It sent a chill through her, thinking about what could have happened to them out there.

"Buzz, Carter, look!" she said, without turning around. She kept her eyes on the spot where the fin had been a second ago.

And then, a few yards farther off, something big burst out of the water. Jane screamed with surprise.

It came straight up, spun all the way around, and splashed down out of sight.

It hadn't been a shark at all, she realized. It was a dolphin. A spinner dolphin. There had been no real danger to begin with.

Before anyone could respond, another dolphin took to the air. And then another, even farther out. Each one of them landed back in the water and continued on its way as smoothly as any gymnast or acrobat.

There seemed to be a whole family of them. Several more surfaced as the pod went by, showing their dorsal fins and expelling air. Jane couldn't tear her eyes away. She wanted to catch as much of the show as possible. The leapers seemed to spin right out of the water for the sheer pleasure of it. They looked so free, so at home here, each one as beautiful as it was amazing to watch.

"Are you guys seeing this?" she asked.

When Buzz finally answered, it wasn't what she expected to hear. "Carter?" he said. And then, "Carter!"

Now Jane did turn around. Her brother was

swaying on his feet, almost as if he were in a trance.

"I think I, uh . . . need to lie down," he said.

Buzz sat up fast, but Carter was already falling. By the time Jane reached for him, Carter's eyes had rolled back in his head. His knees buckled and he dropped, passed out right there on the rocks.

CHAPTER 13

Carter's mind felt like gray fuzz. The fever kept him in a sweat, while the rest of his body seemed to prickle with goose bumps no matter how close to the fire he stayed.

"I think he's awake," someone said.

"Was I asleep?" Carter asked. He remembered stumbling back to the ship, but not much more. "What time is it?"

"The sun's going down," Vanessa said. "Here, we saved you some fish."

"I'll have some later," he said.

"Don't be stupid," she told him. "You have to eat. It's the only way you'll get stronger."

"I'm not being stupid. I'm just not hungry."

"Are you kidding me?" Vanessa asked. She actually seemed angry. Buzz and Jane were sitting across the fire from him, and they noticed it, too. They both looked over now, with scared, wide-eyed expressions.

When Vanessa spoke again, her voice shook. "In case you hadn't noticed, we're all in this together," she said. "We're a family, Carter. How many times do I have to say that before you get it? Now eat the stupid fish before I kill you."

Carter reached over and pinched off a small amount of the flaky white flesh. When he put it in his mouth, it was warm and comforting. But even so, it was hard for him to swallow. His appetite was gone, and he had no desire to eat more. That was as scary as his swollen hand, which was up to twice the size it had been that morning. A line of dried yellow pus showed along the original wound, and it was impossible to unbend his fingers anymore.

Their long day in the sun, and the swim back, had wrecked him. He'd never felt worse, even on the night he'd spewed his guts out after drinking bad water. The difference this time was, he didn't expect to feel better anytime soon.

"Have some more," Vanessa said. She fed him several mouthfuls of fish. Carter took the food, chewed it, and swallowed—but not because he wanted to.

He did it for the others. Right now, that was the most he could manage.

"Buzz, can you give me a hand down here?" Vanessa asked. "I want to pull together whatever bamboo we have."

"There isn't that much," Buzz said.

"Will you just come here, please?" Vanessa asked, more bossy than usual.

She left the deck and dropped to the ground, leading Buzz around the bow to the water's edge, out of earshot from Jane and Carter. All the salvaged bamboo from the raft sat in a pile on the ground against the hull of the ship.

"What's going on?" Buzz asked. "I thought you wanted to—"

Vanessa raised a finger to her mouth to quiet Buzz. "What do we do about Carter?" she whispered.

Buzz shook his head. "What *can* we do?" he whispered back.

Neither of them seemed to have an answer for that. They stared silently at each other. Finally, Vanessa asked the one thing she'd been trying not to bring up for the last three days. She'd been trying not even to think about it, but there was no avoiding the question.

"Can you die from an infected cut?" she asked. The words caught in her throat, followed quickly by a sob. It felt like bringing the possibility to life, just by naming it.

"I don't know," Buzz answered, clearly fighting back his own tears.

"Nobody ever said anything about infection on those million shows you watched?" Vanessa pressed him. "Come on, Buzz, think. There has to be something we can do."

"I don't know!" he said again, in a fierce whisper. "I wish I did, but . . . I don't."

"Is Carter going to die?"

Vanessa turned to see Jane standing there. She'd always had a way of moving around so as to not be noticed. Now she stood in the shadow of the ship's hull, staring at them as if she were afraid to come any closer.

"I hope not," Vanessa answered. Two weeks ago, she would have tried to hide the truth from Jane. Not anymore.

The sound of cicadas filled Vanessa's ears, while horrible thoughts poured into her mind. Would there be a new grave on the island before it was all over? How would they ever be able to take that if it happened? How could they live without Carter?

She shook her head then, as if to expel the thoughts. Up till now, it had been impossible even to imagine something like that happening. But there was also nothing left to say. Nothing they could do, and very little they could even hope for.

Except maybe a miracle.

CHAPTER 14

The next morning, everyone quietly went about his or her business. Vanessa came outside to find Buzz laying pieces of bamboo side by side for a new raft. He'd already split one piece for a new paddle and had begun sharpening another into a spear.

"How long have you been awake?" she asked.

Buzz shook his head. He hadn't slept, she realized. He'd been up all night, sitting with Carter by the fire and working by torchlight.

It swelled her with a melancholy pride. Her little couch potato of a brother had probably changed more than any of them out here. He certainly wasn't a couch potato anymore. And he wasn't giving up, either.

As sad as she felt, she was also glad to have Buzz here, more than ever.

"I don't think we're going to be able to fish today," he said. "What if you and Jane tried to reach the old camp? We could definitely use some coconut to get us by in the meantime."

Vanessa nodded in agreement. There was so much she wanted to say, but Buzz looked as much on edge as she felt. It seemed best to keep moving and try for the coconut. She put a hand on his shoulder, for just a moment, and then turned to go get Jane.

A few minutes later, she and Jane set out through the woods, following the blazed trail back toward the old camp. They were quiet as they walked, each one busy with her own thoughts. Carter still wasn't eating, and had drunk barely any water that morning. When they left him, he'd been dozing fitfully by the fire. The image of his pale, sweaty face haunted Vanessa in the silence.

Soon, they came to the place where the mudslide had been. Water trickled down the slope, and a long muddy scar cut right through the middle of the woods. It didn't take long to figure out that the mud was still too deep to pass.

"Let's check down by the water," Vanessa said. "Maybe we can get over the rocks now."

They cut left and headed downhill. Keeping to the edge of the gully where the mudslide had torn away most of the vegetation, it was an easy pass straight down to the ocean. It only took a few minutes to reach the water.

Coming out into the open, Vanessa stopped again. The warm sunshine felt good on her face. She took a deep breath and closed her eyes.

"Can we sit for a minute?" she asked. "And maybe imagine we're somewhere else?"

"Where?" Jane asked.

"*Anywhere* else."

Even though there were a million things to do, it felt to Vanessa like more than just a good idea. Right now, it felt necessary. Her mind hadn't stopped running since she'd opened her eyes that morning.

Jane didn't say a word. She sat down on a rock,

pulled her knees up tight, and rested her head there.

Vanessa sat down next to her, cross-legged and facing the ocean. She thought about her room back at home. It was strange to imagine it, just sitting there, exactly the way she'd left it, like some kind of movie on pause.

Did her friends even know what was going on? Were the four Benson-Diaz kids in the news? Did everyone think they were dead by now?

This wasn't helping, Vanessa realized. Maybe it was best just to keep moving.

But then Jane sat up all at once. She looked quizzically at Vanessa.

"What is it?" Vanessa asked.

"Do you hear something?" Jane asked.

"Hear what?"

Jane didn't respond right away. She was zoned in, clearly catching something that Vanessa couldn't. Her head was cocked to the side. Her eyes shifted from left to right as if she were trying to envision the image that went with the sound.

"I think that's an airplane!" she said, and jumped up.

Vanessa leaped up as well. She scanned the horizon but didn't see any sign of a plane. It seemed as if Jane were imagining something she wanted to hear.

"I don't know what you're talking about, Jane," she said. "There's nothing there—"

"Shh!" Jane said. "Just listen."

And then, Vanessa heard it, too. The sound was so small, so faint, they might not have even noticed it if they hadn't stopped for a moment of quiet on this piece of shoreline. But there it was, growing clearer as Vanessa listened.

"Where is it? Do you see anything?" Vanessa asked. The sky still looked as empty as the air had sounded a moment ago. But the faint engine sound was undeniable. It had to be somewhere.

"There!" Jane said. She pointed south and west, down the shore.

Vanessa squinted that way—and sure enough, Jane was right again. There it was. How had she seen something so small? It looked like a tiny insect just floating in the distance. But there was no denying what it was. A plane. *A second chance at a rescue.*

Something she'd begun to think they'd never see.

And maybe this time would be different than the last time.

"We have to light the signal fire!" Jane said, just before they both turned back toward the woods.

Even as Vanessa scrambled uphill, headed for camp, she was screaming Buzz's and Carter's names.

Buzz was sitting with Carter on the deck of the ship when the girls came tearing into the cove.

"Buzz! Get a torch!" Jane yelled. "Now! There's a plane!"

"Hurry!" Vanessa yelled. They were climbing down past the spring and gesturing at him frantically.

Buzz didn't fully understand, but he'd heard the only thing he needed to know. *Plane*. Immediately, he was dipping a new torch into the fire.

Even Carter was up now, looking around. "What do we do?" he said, half slurring.

"We have to light the signal fire!" Buzz said. The

oily rags seemed to take forever, but they finally burst to life. He grasped the flaming torch, jumped off the ship, and ran out toward the mouth of the cove.

"Go grab as much wood as you can!" he yelled at the girls, who had started to follow him. "Anything that'll burn! Bring it out to the fire. I'll get it going!"

Jane and Vanessa turned and headed for the ship. Carter was on his way down, already carrying a few logs under his one good arm.

"I'm not even sure if it's coming this way," Jane called back. "But it's definitely out there."

Buzz could hear the hum of the engine as he came to the place where the cove opened up and gave way to the rocky shoreline of the island. In a flat clearing at the top of the rocks, their signal pyre sat waiting.

"Bring the knife!" he shouted back toward the ship. "We need to cut some fronds!" Fresh green fronds made bright white smoke, he knew. Maybe that would help.

He knelt down and pushed the head of the burning torch into the center of the pyre. The ball of dry grass and kindling there sparked up and started burning right away. That was a good sign, but it had a long way to go if there was any hope of catching the plane's attention.

Buzz looked up along the shore. He could see it now. The plane was far off but definitely headed their way.

"BURN!" he yelled at the fire. It seemed to be taking way too long. He could see Jane and Vanessa carrying one of the old wooden pallets together out toward where he stood. Carter came behind, much more slowly.

Buzz left the fire to burn and raced to the ship. When he reached the deck again, he grabbed the bucket of oil and another load of wood and headed back.

"Do you still see the plane?" he shouted as he ran. The signal fire was burning well now, but it didn't look like enough. His heart clenched at the thought of losing another chance at rescue.

"It's coming!" Jane said. "Hurry, Buzz!"

He reached the others and immediately poured the oil around the base of the flames. The heat of the fire singed his arms, but adrenaline kept him going.

The oil sizzled and smoked for several seconds, then ignited with a burst. It let off a trail of dark smoke, but still, it wasn't enough. The plane was well within sight now. He could see the shape of it. But the real question was—how did they make the plane see *them*?

"We need it bigger!" Buzz yelled. "What else have we got to burn?"

"I'll cut some fronds," Vanessa said. She took the knife and scrambled up toward the woods.

Carter tore off his shirt, wiped it around in the oily bucket, and threw it in. Buzz did the same.

"What else?" Buzz asked. It felt as though the clock on their very last chance was ticking down . . . ticking down. . . .

"I have an idea!" Jane shouted. "Come on, Buzz. Right now!"

She grabbed the torch Buzz had been using and headed back toward the ship. Buzz had no clue what she was thinking, but he took off after her. As he left the signal fire behind, Vanessa was throwing fronds down from the woods, and Carter was doing his best to pile them onto the blaze. Just like everything else, it seemed like too little, too late.

Whatever Jane's idea was, he hoped it was a good one.

CHAPTER 15

Buzz followed Jane up onto the boat, into the wheelhouse, and down through the hatch to the deck below. He hated not being able to see outside anymore, not knowing where the plane was.

"What are you doing?" he called after Jane as they moved up the passage toward the stern.

"We're going to light the oil tank!" Jane said.

It stopped Buzz cold. "What?" he asked. "We can't do that."

"We have to," Jane said. She continued into the small cabin with the manhole cover in the floor. It sat over the opening of the tank, just slightly to the side.

Jane set the burning torch on the metal floor and dropped to her knees. "Help me move this out of the way," she said.

"The whole ship could blow up!" Buzz told her.

"Do you have a better idea?" she asked.

He didn't. Jane was right, and Buzz knew it. In fact, he wondered why he hadn't thought of this himself. Fire was his thing. He'd been thinking about how to make and keep fires for the last thirteen days, nonstop. But Jane's calm focus, despite the urgency of the situation, was infectious.

He knelt down next to her and put his hands on the heavy iron disc. "One, two, three!" he said. They heaved together and twisted the cover off to the side. The smell from down below burned Buzz's nostrils.

Outside, he could hear the sound of the plane. It was getting close.

"Okay," Jane said as she picked up the torch. "Get ready to run like crazy."

"Wait!" Buzz said. He knew what to do. There was no reason for two of them to be down here right now. He reached out and snatched the torch away.

"What are you doing?" Jane said.

"Go," Buzz told her. "I'll light it."

"But—" Jane started to object.

"There's no time, Jane," Buzz cut her off. "Just go. I'll catch up."

"Buzz, you can't!" she said.

He dropped the torch on the floor, put both hands on her shoulders, and shoved her toward the door. "GET OUT!" he screamed. "You're wasting time. Go!"

Jane stumbled into the passage and let out a wail as she ran toward the front.

"Hurry, Buzz!" she called back. "Please hurry!"

Buzz stood in the middle of the cabin and picked up the burning torch. He knew that it usually took a moment before the oil caught fire. With any luck, he'd have just enough time to get out of there. And if not, it could still get the others off this island, once and for all. That was a risk worth taking, especially for Carter's sake. He wouldn't survive much longer.

This was it. One chance to save them. It was crazy—a complete shot in the dark. But Jane was right. They had to try.

He could hear Jane outside now screaming for the others. That was good. It meant she was off the boat.

Buzz checked the door once more to make sure he had a clear way out of the room.

He held the torch over the hole. He positioned his feet like a sprinter ready to fly. Then he took a deep breath and dropped the torch down into the tank.

Vanessa could scarcely believe what Jane was telling her.

"Yes, he's lighting the fuel tank!" she said again. "I'm sorry, it was my idea!"

Vanessa turned toward the ship, running blindly. The plane—headed straight for the island—was forgotten. She had to get Buzz out of there. This was insane.

"Buzz!" she screamed, splashing along the edge of the cove. "Buzz! Don't do it! Get out of there!"

She was halfway back to the boat when she saw Buzz racing through the wheelhouse on his way out.

"Run!" Buzz screamed. He threw himself off the deck and kept going. "Get away, get away, get away!"

Vanessa stopped and reversed direction, with Buzz right behind. The plane was almost directly overhead. If the ship was going to blow it needed to blow now.

"Nothing's happening!" Buzz said, even as they were still moving.

"Are you sure you lit it?" Vanessa said back.

"I don't know, I put the—"

A giant, hollow explosion of sound filled the air. The force of it blew through the cove like a strong wind. Vanessa felt her ears pop. She stumbled just as Buzz caught up to her. They both hit the ground, then turned to look back.

A giant, rolling red-and-orange ball was rising up from the ship. It looked as if the sky itself was on fire. It was huge. The wheelhouse had disintegrated. Vanessa threw an arm over Buzz as debris splashed down in the water and onto the ground around them. A giant piece of railing landed with a crash, just ten feet off to the right.

When she looked up again, Vanessa saw the rolling flames giving way to a black smoke that flowed up and out of the cove, like fumes through a chimney. If anything was going to be seen from a distance, it wasn't their signal fire anymore. It was that explosion.

Adrenaline still pumping, Vanessa grabbed Buzz's hand and ran back to the others.

"YES!" Jane shouted as Buzz and Vanessa raced toward them. It had worked. Somehow, it had worked.

But they weren't through this yet. She stood at the water's edge with Carter, waving and waving at the plane. This was it—the moment when it all came to an end. It had to be. There was no other option, and they all screamed at the sky.

"HELP!"

"DOWN HERE!"

"PLEASE!"

Unbelievably, the airplane never changed its

course. It continued on its way, passing west over the island, while the screaming continued.

"NO! DON'T LEAVE!"

"COME BACK!"

But it was no good. Within a few moments, the plane had disappeared over the tops of the trees. Jane stood with her neck still craned upward, her gaze overhead, where there was nothing left to see anymore.

The plane was gone. Not only that, but the ship was ruined as well. It was all too much—an unbearable load of bad luck. She couldn't hold back her tears.

"I don't understand," she sobbed. "How could they not see us? How could this happen—again?"

"Was it the same plane as the last time?" Vanessa asked.

"I don't know," Jane said. "What does it matter?"

"It doesn't," Vanessa said. "I just . . ." She trailed off, as if she'd realized there was nothing left to say. No way to describe what any of them were feeling. And now she was crying, too. They all were.

It couldn't be true. The plane couldn't have really passed them by. Not *twice*.

And yet, the empty sky over Jane's head told her everything there was to know. The plane had moved on, and the only thing up there now was a huge black cloud of smoke, as the ship behind them—their home—burned up in flames.

Just like their chances of being rescued.

Carter didn't even try to wipe away his tears. The pain in his hand was nothing compared to the torture of watching another rescue slip right through their fingers.

And there had been nothing he could do to help. All he'd managed was a few weak shouts at the sky, watching the speck of a plane fly over, with a horrible sense of déjà vu.

He lay back on the rocks now, feeling empty. Not just in his stomach, but in his heart, too. Everywhere. Everything. The emptiness consumed him. It felt . . . over.

Nobody said a word for a long time. They all sank

to the ground around him, catching their breath at first, then crying quietly to themselves. There was simply nothing to say.

In fact, if there had been any conversation, Carter might not have heard the soft hum of the plane, coming closer again.

But he did hear it. At first, he stayed silent, thinking it might just be his imagination playing tricks on him. It wasn't until he saw Buzz look up, and then both of the girls, too, that he let himself believe it might be true.

"Is that . . . ?" Buzz said.

"Really?" Jane said, turning around in a full circle, scanning the sky again.

There was no mistaking it now. The plane had looped around from the west and was headed back in their direction.

"They must have seen the smoke!" Vanessa said. "That has to be it!"

"They're coming back! They're coming back!" Jane sang out.

And then sure enough, over the tops of the trees, the beautiful sight of an airplane appeared. It was flying lower than before—much lower. This was a plane getting ready to land. But where? There wasn't enough room on the island.

Carter could see now that this wasn't the same craft from the other day. It was red and white, with big pontoons underneath. This was a seaplane—it could land on water.

He waved, while his brother and sisters jumped up and down, screaming as loudly as they could.

It was an unbelievable sight. An unbelievable feeling, too. Like some kind of dream he'd had more than once since they'd landed on Nowhere Island. And now it was coming true.

The plane flew in a wide arc, out over the ocean to the east, and then back again, heading straight at them. The others held Carter up on his feet as it skimmed down onto the water, propellers buzzing, less than fifty yards offshore.

It was hard for Carter to make out what Vanessa and Buzz were even saying, there was so much excitement in their voices. Jane was crying too hard for words.

He could see the pilot behind the seaplane's small windshield. There were others on board as well, moving around inside as they continued to float closer. Soon, the door on the side opened.

And even now, with everything that had just happened, the last person Carter expected to see was the first off the plane.

"MOMMY!" Jane screamed, finding her voice.

Beth Benson reached toward them, still twenty yards away, her face crumpled up with tears of her own. Behind her, Eric Diaz emerged onto the pontoon.

"Dad!" Buzz and Vanessa yelled simultaneously.

Behind their parents, two of the flight crew had already launched a bright yellow dinghy. One of them was handing red-and-white boxes of what Carter guessed to be medical supplies down to the other.

But Mom wasn't waiting. She plunged into the water followed by Dad, and they started swimming for the beach.

It was too much for Carter. It was as if his mind didn't know how to process what was happening. All the fears—that they might never be rescued, that his infection might kill him—were gone. The feeling went way beyond words. There were only tears now.

Tears of joy.

Vanessa, Jane, and Buzz raced into the water toward their parents. Carter was moving, too, more slowly. Before they'd gotten very far, Buzz stopped and turned around to come back. He put an arm around Carter to hold him up, and they continued on together.

"We did it, Carter," Buzz said. "I don't know how—but we did."

Before Carter could say anything, they were both swallowed up in their parents' arms. Jane and Vanessa were there, too—a six-person huddle of tears and screams, with everyone talking at once.

"It's a miracle!" Dad said.

"How'd you find us?" Vanessa asked.

"You're here, you're here! You're really here!" Jane cheered.

"Look at you!" Mom said. "I can't believe this!"

"We're okay," Buzz was saying. "I think we're okay."

Only Carter stayed silent. His legs wobbled

underneath him, while the others held him up. His hand throbbed as badly as ever, and the fever put a soft blur on everything he saw and heard around him. He wasn't out of the woods yet. He knew that.

But he'd never felt so safe in his life as he did right now.

CHAPTER 16

July 11. LAST DAY ON NOWHERE ISLAND

You know what's better than snails??? Peanut M&M's. And bottled water. And turkey sandwiches. And granola bars.

And having my mom and dad right here in front of my eyes. And hugging them, and knowing I never have to stop if I don't want to.

And my mom's voice telling me everything is going to be okay again.

And knowing that we're going home.

I'm going to write that again. WE'RE GOING HOME.

Mom told me that Joe and Uncle Dex are safe and sound. They had to go to the hospital for a little while, but they're going to be just fine. She also said that she and Dad have been flying their own hired plane all over the place for days—even double-checking the sections that the Coast Guard had already checked. And guess what? It worked, because here they are.

Carter's in the worst shape, by far. I'm watching them give him intravenous medicine and taking good care of him, right here on the island. The floatplane is too small for all of us, so the pilots are going to fly back and get a helicopter to come pick us up! I've never been in a helicopter!

Good-bye, snails. Good-bye, mud and rain and mosquitoes, and grubs and snakes and ants, and wild boars and everything else about this place. I won't ever forget you, Nowhere Island, but I can't wait to start trying.

Already, Mom and Dad have a million questions. Mostly they want to know how we did this.

Dad said, "You guys are a real miracle. How did you survive?"

And I liked Buzz's answer.

He said, "Together."

READ HOW THE ADVENTURE BEGAN IN

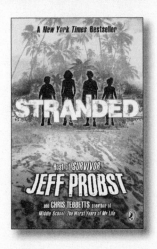

A family vacation becomes a test of survival.

It was supposed to be a vacation—and a chance to get to know one another better. But when a massive storm sets in without warning, four kids are shipwrecked alone on a rocky jungle island in the middle of the South Pacific. No adults. No instructions. Nobody to rely upon but themselves. Can they make it home alive?

A week ago, the biggest challenge Vanessa, Buzz, Carter, and Jane had was learning to live as a new blended family. Now the four siblings must find a way to work together if they're going to make it off the island. But first they've got to learn to survive one another.

CHAPTER 1

It was day four at sea, and as far as eleven-year-old Carter Benson was concerned, life didn't get any better than this.

From where he hung, suspended fifty feet over the deck of the *Lucky Star*, all he could see was a planet's worth of blue water. The boat's huge white mainsail ballooned in front of him, filled with a stiff southerly wind that sent them scudding through the South Pacific faster than they'd sailed all week.

This was the best part of the best thing Carter had ever done, no question. It was like sailing and flying at the same time. The harness around his middle held him in place while his arms and legs hung free. The air itself seemed to carry him along, at speed with the boat.

"How you doin' up there, Carter?" Uncle Dexter shouted from the cockpit.

Carter flashed a thumbs-up and pumped his fist. "Faster!" he shouted back. Even with the wind whipping in his ears, Dex's huge belly laugh came back, loud and clear.

Meanwhile, Carter had a job to do. He wound the safety line from his harness in a figure eight around the cleat on the mast to secure himself. Then he reached over and unscrewed the navigation lamp he'd come up here to replace.

As soon as he'd pocketed the old lamp in his rain slicker, he pulled out the new one and fitted it into the fixture, making sure not to let go before he'd tightened it down. Carter had changed plenty of lightbulbs before, but never like this. If anything, it was all too easy and over too fast.

When he was done, he unwound his safety line and gave a hand signal to Dex's first mate, Joe

Kahali, down below. Joe put both hands on the winch at the base of the mast and started cranking Carter back down to the deck.

"Good job, Carter," Joe said, slapping him on the back as he got there. Carter swelled with pride and adrenaline. Normally, replacing the bulb would have been Joe's job, but Dex trusted him to take care of it.

Now Joe jerked a thumb over his shoulder. "Your uncle wants to talk to you," he said.

Carter stepped out of the harness and stowed it in its locker, just like Dex and Joe had trained him to do. Once that was done, he clipped the D-ring on his life jacket to the safety cable that ran the length of the deck and headed toward the back.

It wasn't easy to keep his footing as the *Lucky Star* pitched and rolled over the waves, but even that was part of the fun. If he did fall, the safety cable—also called a jackline—would keep him from going over-board. Everyone was required to stay clipped in when they were on deck, whether they were up there to work . . . or to puke, like Buzz was doing right now.

"Gross! Watch out, Buzz!" Carter said, pushing past him.

"*Uhhhhhnnnnh,*" was all Buzz said in return. He was leaning against the rail and looked both green and gray at the same time.

Carter kind of felt sorry for him. They were both eleven years old, but they didn't really have anything else in common. It was like they were having two different vacations out here.

"Gotta keep moving," he said, and continued on toward the back, where Dex was waiting.

"Hey, buddy, it's getting a little choppier than I'd like," Dex said as Carter stepped down into the cockpit. "I need you guys to get below."

"I don't want to go below," Carter said. "Dex, I can help. Let me steer!"

"No way," Dex said. "Not in this wind. You've been great, Carter, but I promised your mom before we set sail—no kids on deck if these swells got over six feet. You see that?" He pointed to the front of the boat, where a cloud of sea spray had just broken over the bow. "*That's* what a six-foot swell looks like. We've got a storm on the way—maybe a big one. It's time for you to take a break."

"Come on, please?" Carter said. "I thought we came out here to sail!"

Dex took him by the shoulders and looked him square in the eye.

"Remember what we talked about before we set out? My boat. My rules. Got it?"

Carter got it, all right. Arguing with Dex was like wrestling a bear. You could try, but you were never going to win.

"Now, grab your brother and get down there," Dex told him.

"Okay, fine," Carter said. "But he's not my brother, by the way. Just because my mom married his dad doesn't mean—"

"Ask me tomorrow if I care," Dexter said, and gave him a friendly but insistent shove. "Now go!"

Benjamin "Buzz" Diaz lifted his head from the rail

and looked out into the distance. All he could see from here was an endless stretch of gray clouds over an endless stretch of choppy waves.

Keeping an eye on the horizon was supposed to help with the seasickness, but so far, all it had done was remind him that he was in the middle of the biggest stretch of nowhere he'd ever seen. His stomach felt like it had been turned upside down and inside out. His legs were like rubber bands, and his head swam with a thick, fuzzy feeling, while the boat rocked and rocked and rocked.

It didn't look like this weather was going to be changing anytime soon, either. At least, not for the better.

Buzz tried to think about something else—anything else—to take his mind off how miserable he felt. He thought about his room back home. He thought about how much he couldn't wait to get there, where he could just close his door and hang out all day if he wanted, playing City of Doom and eating pepperoni pizz—

Wait, Buzz thought. *No. Not that.*

He tried to unthink anything to do with food, but it was too late. Already, he was leaning over the rail again and hurling the last of his breakfast into the ocean.

"Still feeding the fish, huh?" Suddenly, Carter was back. He put a hand on Buzz's arm. "Come on," he said. "Dex told me we have to get below."

Buzz clutched his belly. "Are you kidding?" he said. "Can't it wait?"

"No. Come on."

All week long, Carter had been running around the deck of the *Lucky Star* like he owned it or something. Still, Carter was the least of Buzz's worries right now.

It was only day four at sea, and if things kept going like this, he was going to be lucky to make it to day five.

Vanessa Diaz sat at the *Lucky Star*'s navigation station belowdecks and stared at the laptop screen in front of her. She'd only just started to learn about this stuff a few days earlier, but as far as she could tell, all that orange and red on the weather radar was a bad sign. Not to mention the scroll across the bottom of the screen, saying something about "gale-force winds and deteriorating conditions."

The first three days of their trip had been nothing but clear blue skies and warm breezes. Now, nine hundred miles off the coast of Hawaii, all of that had changed. Dexter kept saying they had to adjust their course to outrun the weather, but so far, it seemed like the weather was outrunning them. They'd changed direction at least three times, and things only seemed to be getting worse.

The question was—how *much* worse?

A chill ran down Vanessa's spine as the hatch over the galley stairs opened, and Buzz and Carter came clattering down the steps.

"How are you feeling, Buzzy?" she asked, but he didn't stop to talk. Instead, he went straight for the little bathroom—the "head," Dexter called it—and slammed the door behind him.

Her little brother was getting the worst of these bad seas, by far. Carter, on the other hand, seemed unfazed.

Sometimes Vanessa called them "the twins," as a joke, because they were both eleven but nothing alike. Carter kept his sandy hair cut short and was even kind of muscley for a kid his age. Buzz, on the other hand, had shaggy jet-black curls like their father's and was what adults liked to call husky. The kids at school just called him fat.

Vanessa didn't think her brother was fat—not exactly—but you could definitely tell he spent a lot of time in front of the TV.

"It's starting to rain," Carter said, looking up at the sky.

"Then close the hatch," Vanessa said.

"Don't tell me what to do."

Vanessa rolled her eyes. "Okay, fine. Get wet. See if I care."

He would, too, she thought. He'd just stand there and get rained on, only because she told him not to. Carter was one part bulldog and one part mule.

Jane was there now, too. She'd just come out of the tiny sleeping cabin the two girls shared.

Jane was like the opposite of Carter. She could slip in and out of a room without anyone ever noticing. With Carter, you always knew he was there.

"What are you looking at, Nessa?" Jane asked.

"Nothing." Vanessa flipped the laptop closed. "I was just checking the weather," she said.

There was no reason to scare Jane about all that. She was only nine, and tiny for her age. Vanessa was the oldest, at thirteen, and even though nobody told her to look out for Jane on this trip, she did anyway.

"Dex said there's a storm coming," Carter blurted out. "He said it's going to be major."

"Carter!" Vanessa looked over at him and rolled her eyes in Jane's direction.

But he just shrugged. "What?" he said. "You think she's not going to find out?"

"You don't have to worry about me," Jane said.

She crawled up onto Vanessa's lap and opened the computer to have a look. "Show me."

"See?" Carter said. "I know my sister."

Vanessa took a deep breath. If the idea of this trip was to make them one big happy family, it wasn't exactly working.

Technically, the whole sailing adventure was a wedding gift from her new uncle, Dexter. It had been two months since Vanessa and Buzz's father had married Carter and Jane's mother, but they'd waited until the end of the school year to take a honeymoon. Now, while their parents were hiking Volcanoes National Park and enjoying the beaches on Hawaii's Big Island, the four kids were spending the week at sea and supposedly getting to know one another better.

So far, the sailing had been amazing, but the sister-brother bonding thing? Not so much, Vanessa thought. The weather wasn't helping, either. It looked like they were going to be cooped up together for the rest of the day.

"Is that the storm?" Jane said. She pointed at the large red mass on the laptop screen.

"That's it," Vanessa answered. On the computer, it seemed as if the oncoming front had gotten even bigger in the last few minutes. She started braiding Jane's long blond hair to distract her.

"It's just rain, right?" Jane said. "If this was something really bad, we'd already know about it. Wouldn't we, Nessa?"

Vanessa tried to smile. "Sure," she said. But the truth was, she had no idea how bad it was going to get.

None of them did.

GET MORE OF THE ADVENTURE IN

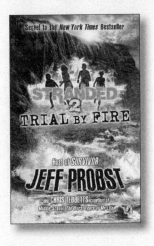

They thought it couldn't get any worse. They were wrong.

Being shipwrecked on a jungle island in the middle of the South Pacific was bad enough. But now that Carter, Vanessa, Buzz, and Jane have lost their boat—and almost everything on board—to another violent storm, it's like starting over. That means finding food and shelter, making fire for the first time, dealing with the wild boars that roam the island—and of course, figuring out how to get along (and not kill each other in the process). Survival is no individual sport in a place like this, but there's only one way to learn that. The hard way.